Teacher Resource Copymasters

HOUGHTON MIFFLIN Math Steps

HOUGHTON MIFFLIN

Boston • Atlanta • Dallas • Denver • Geneva, Illinois • Palo Alto • Princeton

Contents

Assessments

The assessment copymasters give you valuable information about your students' prior knowledge, progress, and understanding of new mathematical content.

From the beginning of the year through the end of the year, you can assess students' understanding of mathematical skills, concepts, and vocabulary. Both free-response and multiple-choice tests are provided.

The results of these tests can help you assess whether students have the necessary prerequisite skills and knowledge in order to be successful with this year's materials, whether students are progressing adequately, and whether students have achieved the goals of the mathematics curriculum.

Reteach Worksheets

Reteach Worksheets meet the needs of students who require reinforcement of topics or concepts. The step-by-step instruction on each worksheet supports students through the learning process. The Teacher Note at the bottom of each page tells you when to use the Worksheet.

Some Reteach Worksheets review prerequisite skills or concepts for a unit. Students can use these before they begin a unit.

Most Reteach Worksheets support lessons in a unit. In the Student Book, there is a Quick Check feature that appears at the end of many lessons. The Quick Check reviews the lessons you have just covered. If students have difficulty with any of the concepts or skills on the Quick Check, they can use the Reteach Worksheets that correspond to the items. References to Reteach Worksheets appear in the Teacher Edition in both the Annotated Student Book pages and in the Lesson Support.

Extension Worksheets cover a variety of mathematical content. They give students an opportunity to extend the topic they are learning or they introduce students to new topics.

The Extension Worksheets are organized by unit. The Teacher Note at the bottom of each page tells you when to use the Worksheet. References to Extension Worksheets appear in the Lesson Support in the Teacher Edition.

Teaching Resources are copymasters for frequently used teaching aids and for Family Projects. You may use the teaching aids during the presentation of a lesson or reproduce them for students to use individually. Family Projects provide suggestions for students and their families to work together on the skills and objectives in each unit.

Answer Keys include answers for all of the assessments, as well as the Reteach Worksheets and Extension Worksheets.

Assessments

NOTES

Assessment Overview

At the Beginning of the Year

- **Beginning of the Year Inventory**

  Before your students start Unit 1, you may give them the Beginning of the Year Inventory. This pretest shows whether students possess the necessary prerequisite skills and knowledge to be successful with this year's mathematics.

  You can also use the Inventory as a placement test for students who transfer to your school during the schoolyear.

  The Inventory uses free-response format to test objectives that cover skills, concepts, problem solving, and vocabulary.

Before Each Unit

- **Unit Pretest**

  Assessing prior knowledge helps you build effective lessons using what students already know. You will quickly learn which skills, concepts, and vocabulary your students need to review before they begin a new unit.

  By using the results of the Unit Pretests, you can prepare your students to be confident and successful with the mathematics in the new unit.

During Each Unit

- **Quick Checks in the Student Book**

  Monitor and assess students' progress at regular intervals. The Quick Check reviews the lessons you have just covered.

  References to the Reteach Worksheets and the Skills Tutorial appear in the Teacher Edition in both the Annotated Student Book pages and in the Lesson Support.

After Each Unit

- **Unit Posttest**

  Each Unit Posttest is an additional tool you may use to assess students' mathematical understanding and application of the work in that unit.

  The Unit Posttests are formatted like the Unit Reviews in the Student Book and cover all unit objectives.

At Midyear

- **Midyear Test**

  The Midyear Test covers objectives from Units 1 through 6 in the Student Book. Test results will show which skills or concepts you need to review with students.

  This test is in standardized format to provide your students with valuable experience in taking standardized tests. Students will mark their answers on the answer sheet provided (see Teaching Resource 2) by filling in the space for their answer choice.

At the End of the Year

- **Final Test**

  The Final Test covers objectives from Units 7 through 11 in the Student Book, as well as key objectives from each unit in the first half of the book.

  You can use this summative test to reinforce the topics taught throughout the year and to assess what students have mastered.

  The Final Test is in standardized format to provide your students with more test-taking practice. Students will mark their answers on the answer sheet provided (see Teaching Resource 2) by filling in the space for their answer choice.

4

Complete.

1. $2 + 5 =$ _____   **2.** $6 + 4 =$ _____   **3.** $9 + 3 =$ _____

4. $5 +$ _____ $= 10$ **5.** $6 +$ _____ $= 14$ **6.** $3 +$ _____ $= 9$

7. _____ $+ 8 = 12$ **8.** _____ $+ 9 = 18$ **9.** _____ $+ 7 = 15$

10. 1 minute = _____ seconds   **11.** 1 hour = _____ minutes

12. 1 day = _____ hours   **13.** 1 week = _____ days

14. 1 year = _____ months   **15.** 1 year = _____ days

Complete the fact family.

16. _____ $+$ 4 $=$ 9

_____ $+$ _____ $=$ _____

9 $-$ _____ $=$ _____

_____ $-$ _____ $=$ _____

17. 0 $+$ _____ $=$ 6

_____ $+$ _____ $=$ _____

6 $-$ _____ $=$ _____

_____ $-$ _____ $=$ _____

18. _____ $+$ 9 $=$ _____

_____ $+$ _____ $=$ 16

16 $-$ _____ $=$ _____

_____ $-$ _____ $=$ _____

19. 7 $+$ _____ $=$ 13

_____ $+$ _____ $=$ _____

13 $-$ _____ $=$ _____

_____ $-$ _____ $=$ _____

Identify the figure.

20.

21.

22.

23.

_____   _____   _____   _____

24. Loop the figures that can roll.

25. Loop the figures with corners.

  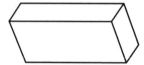

26. Write the amount.
4 dimes, 1 nickel, 3 pennies = _____

Write the number.

27.

_____

28.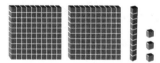

_____

29.

_____

30. 50 + 2 = _____

31. 300 + 80 + 6 = _____

32. 900 + 2 = _____

33. ninety-three _____

34. one hundred thirty _____

35. four hundred eight _____

36. six hundred twelve _____

37. five hundred four _____

Compare. Write <, >, or =.

38. 560 ◯ 559   **39.** 113 ◯ 131   **40.** 72 ◯ 70 + 2

41. 286 ◯ 386   **42.** $.62 ◯ $.71   **43.** $.25 ◯ $.19

Write the number in words.

44. 75 _____   **45.** 202 _____

Round each number to the nearest ten.

46. 69 → _____   **47.** 23 → _____   **48.** 45 → _____

Round each number to the nearest hundred.

49. 128 → _____   **50.** 360 → _____   **51.** 553 → _____

Round each number to the nearest thousand.

52. 1,481 → _____   **53.** 2,399 → _____   **54.** 3,802 → _____

Measure the segment in centimeters.

55. ├──────────────────┤   _____ cm

Compare the weight of the object to a pound.
Write *more than*, *less than*, or *about equal*.

56.   **57.**   **58.**

_____   _____   _____

Measure the segment in inches.

59. ├────────────────────────────┤

_____ in.

60. **Count by 2's.**

2									

61. **Count by 3's.**

3									

62. **Count by 5's.**

5									

63. **Count by 10's.**

10									

Add.

64. $4 + 4 + 6 =$ _____ **65.** $6 + 2 + 5 =$ _____ **66.** $5 + 1 + 8 =$ _____

67.
$$\begin{array}{r} 32 \\ + 15 \\ \hline \end{array}$$

68.
$$\begin{array}{r} 44 \\ + 35 \\ \hline \end{array}$$

69.
$$\begin{array}{r} 34 \\ 12 \\ + 21 \\ \hline \end{array}$$

70.
$$\begin{array}{r} 32 \\ 24 \\ + 43 \\ \hline \end{array}$$

71.
$$\begin{array}{r} 29 \\ + \ 8 \\ \hline \end{array}$$

72.
$$\begin{array}{r} 64 \\ + 28 \\ \hline \end{array}$$

73.
$$\begin{array}{r} 18 \\ + 38 \\ \hline \end{array}$$

74.
$$\begin{array}{r} 59 \\ + 73 \\ \hline \end{array}$$

Use mental math to add or subtract.

75. $30 + 45 =$ _____ **76.** $86 - 50 =$ _____ **77.** $72 - 20 =$ _____

78. $24 + 53 =$ _____ **79.** $67 - 47 =$ _____ **80.** $43 + 16 =$ _____

Subtract.

81. 38
− 16

82. 49
− 22

83. 56
− 31

84. 98
− 45

85. 64
− 25

86. 90
− 36

87. 71
− 47

88. 82
− 29

Write the time.

89.

_____

90.

_____

91.

_____

92. What time will it be in three hours?

_____

Write the fraction that tells how much is shaded.

93.

_____

94.

_____

95.

_____

Add or subtract.

96. $5.26
+ 1.23

97. $3.16
+ 2.32

98. $6.83
− 2.51

99. $1.96
− .35

Complete.

100. 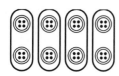 $2 + 2 + 2 + 2 =$ _____ $4 \times 2 =$ _____

4 twos = _____   4 sets of 2 = _____

Write the product.

101. $3 \times 2 =$ _____   **102.** $4 \times 5 =$ _____   **103.** $3 \times 10 =$ _____

$1 \times 2 =$ _____ $2 \times 5 =$ _____ $0 \times 10 =$ _____

6	1	5
$\times\ 2$	$\times\ 5$	$\times\ 10$

0	3	1
$\times\ 2$	$\times\ 5$	$\times\ 10$

5	0	2
$\times\ 2$	$\times\ 5$	$\times\ 10$

Complete.

104  $10 \div 2 =$ _____

Decide if the event will sometimes, always, or never happen.
Write *sometimes, always,* or *never*.

105.   The sky will be green at noon. _____

It will rain when it is windy. _____

A rock will sink in a pond. _____

You toss a coin. It will land heads. _____

Solve.

106. There are **2** boxes of apples. There are **6** apples in each box. How many apples are there? Draw a picture to solve.

_____

107. Four houses on one side of a street are numbered **28, 30, 32,** and **34.** If the pattern continues, what is the number of the fifth house?

_____

108. A hot dog costs **$.40.** A juice box costs **$.30.** A banana costs **$.20.** Claire bought **2** items. She spent **$.60.** What did she buy?

_____

109. Jason took **14** pictures. Elaine took **8** pictures. How may more pictures did Jason take? Write a number sentence to solve.

_____

_____

110. Osamu has **8** model cars. He gets **4** more model cars for his birthday. How many model cars does he have now?

_____

111. Natalie must read **16** pages. She has already read **9** pages. How many pages does she have left to read?

_____

112. There are **38** chairs in the room. Only **6** are not being used. How many chairs are being used?

_____

113. A florist has **50** roses. Thirty of the roses are red. The other roses are white. Are there more white roses or red roses?

_____

Solve. Use the bar graph.

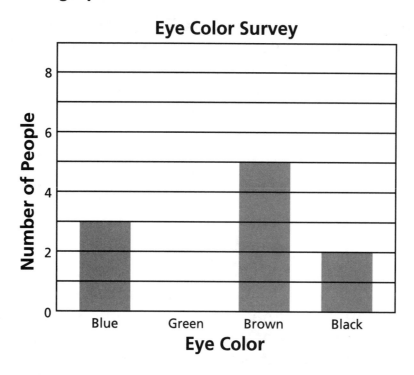

Eye Color Survey

Number of People

Blue   Green   Brown   Black

Eye Color

114. How many people have brown eyes?

_____

115. How many people have blue eyes or black eyes?

_____

116. How many more people have blue eyes than green eyes?

_____

117. What color eyes do the most people have?

_____

118. What color eyes do the fewest people have?

_____

119. How many people took part in the survey?

_____

How many blocks? Give the standard form. (1A)

1.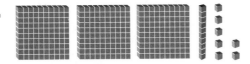

_____

2.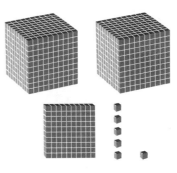

_____

Complete. (1B)

	Th	H	T	O
3. 648 =		6	4	8
4. 71 =				
5. ___ =	2	5	1	3
6. 4,925 =	4	9	2	5

3. or ___ + ___ + ___

4. or **70 + 1**

5. or **2,000 + 500 + 10 + 3**

6. or ___ + ___ + ___ + ___

How much money? Use $ and . to give the amount. (1E)

7.

_____

8.

_____

Continue the number sequence. (1C)

9. 67, 68, _____, _____, _____, _____

10. 430, 440, _____, _____, _____, _____

11. 5,100, 5,200, _____, _____, _____, _____

Compare. Use <, >, or =. (1C)

12. 38 ◯ 35

290 ◯ 290

5,116 ◯ 6,114

13. 76 ◯ 79

481 ◯ 480

21,743 ◯ 21,473

14. 62,101 ◯ 62,110

1,362 ◯ 1,623

89,402 ◯ 98,402

Write these times two ways. (1F)

15.

_____

or _____

16.

_____

or _____

17.

_____

or _____

Complete the sentences. (1D)

18. _____ is the **5th** day of the week.

19. Saturday is the _____ day after Wednesday.

20. Which days begin with the letters *M, W,* and *F*? Use ordinal numbers.

_____

Days of the Week	
1st	Sunday
2nd	Monday
3rd	Tuesday
4th	Wednesday
5th	Thursday
6th	Friday
7th	Saturday

Solve. (1F, 1G)

21. Katie jogs on these days of the month: **1st, 4th, 7th, 10th, 13th,** and so on. What pattern do you see?

_____

22. Bryce eats breakfast at **7:45** A.M. In **12** hours what time will it be? Is it A.M. or P.M.?

_____

How many blocks? Give the standard form. (1A)

1.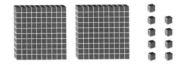

_____

2.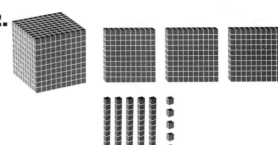

_____

Complete. (1B)

		Th	H	T	O	
3.	297 =		2	9	7	or _____ + _____ + _____
4.	36 =					or 30 + 6
5.	_____ =	5	2	7	9	or 5,000 + 200 + 70 + 9
6.	1,862 =	1	8	6	2	or _____ + _____ + _____ + _____

How much money? Use $ and . to give the amount. (1E)

7.

_____

8.

_____

Continue the number sequence. (1C)

9. 88, 89, _____, _____, _____, _____

10. 340, 350, _____, _____, _____, _____

11. 3,300, 3,400, _____, _____, _____, _____

Compare. Use <, >, or =. (1C)

12. 52 ◯ 54

320 ◯ 230

4,218 ◯ 4,220

13. 19 ◯ 13

580 ◯ 579

19,483 ◯ 18,843

14. 40,271 ◯ 40,271

3,915 ◯ 3,951

603,591 ◯ 630,591

Write these times two ways. (1F)

15.

_____

or _____

16.

4:50

_____

or _____

17.

_____

or _____

Complete the sentences. (1D)

18. _____ is the **3rd** day of the week.

19. Friday is the _____ day after Monday.

20. Which days begin with the letters *M* and *T*? Use ordinal numbers.

_____

_____

Days of the Week	
1st	Sunday
2nd	Monday
3rd	Tuesday
4th	Wednesday
5th	Thursday
6th	Friday
7th	Saturday

Solve. (1F, 1G)

21. Clark mows his lawn on these days of the month: **1st, 7th, 13th, 19th, 25th,** and so on. What pattern do you see?

_____

22. Caitlin eats lunch at **11:45** A.M. In **12** hours what time will it be? Is it A.M. or P.M.?

_____

Add. Remember to regroup. (2A, 2D)

1. 284
+ 163

2. 376
+ 457

3. $1.29
+ 2.65

4. 263
+ 178

5. 3,819
+ 2,194

6. $2.68
+ 4.95

7. 173
+ 642

8. 3,458
+ 5,136

9. $2.45
+ 1.82

10. 327
+ 299

11. $5.68
+ 2.93

12. 1,364
+ 3,584

Round to the underlined place. (2B)

13. 4̲6 → _____

14. 2̲,359 → _____

15. 3̲2̲2 → _____

16. 8̲31 → _____

17. 1,̲554 → _____

18. 6,2̲3̲5 → _____

Round to the nearest ten. Estimate each sum. (2C)

19. 72 →
+ 56 → ____

20. 134 →
+ 18 → ____

21. 89 →
+ 27 → ____

Solve. (2E)

22. Lindsay picks a **2-digit number.** She writes the number three times and finds that the sum is **258.** What is the number? What strategy did you use?

23. Tysen estimates to the nearest ten that he has about **40** basketball cards in his sports card collection. What is the greatest number of basketball cards he could have? What is the least number?

Add. Remember to regroup. (2A, 2D)

1. 176
      + 118

2. 254
      + 379

3. $2.48
      + 1.91

4. 327
      + 216

5. 4,285
      + 3,698

6. $5.58
      + 2.89

7. 283
      + 464

8. 1,629
      + 6,299

9. $3.19
      + 1.99

10. 263
       + 184

11. $5.75
       + 3.59

12. 2,753
       + 4,295

Round to the underlined place. (2B)

13. 2̲9 → _____

14. 1̲,438 → _____

15. 71̲6 → _____

16. 9̲25 → _____

17. 3,6̲84 → _____

18. 2,18̲5 → _____

Round to the nearest ten. Estimate each sum. (2C)

19. 85 →
      + 19 → ____

20. 114 →
       + 18 → ____

21. 92 →
       + 36 → ____

Solve. (2E)

22. Shauna picks a **2**-digit number. She writes the number three times and finds that the sum is **117.** What is the number? What strategy did you use?

_____

_____

23. Taylor estimates to the nearest ten that he has about **30** airplane models. What is the greatest number of models he could have? What is the least number?

_____

_____

Subtract. (3A)

1. $5.36
   − 2.58

2. 704
   − 146

3. $3.59
   − 1.23

4. $8.05
   − .48

5. 631
   − 8

6. $9.02
   − 3.26

7. 473
   − 192

8. 601
   − 273

9. $5.65
   − 2.83

10. $14.00
   − 11.86

11. 877
   − 618

12. 306
   − 58

13. 642
   − 105

14. 380
   − 148

15. 1,529
   − 89

16. $7.50
   − .64

17. 1,500
   − 249

18. 800
   − 427

19. 2,600
   − 399

20. 4,500
   − 2,438

Estimate the difference. (3B)

21. 68 →
   − 17 → _____

22. 98 →
   − 24 → _____

23. 73 →
   − 41 → _____

Solve. (3C)

24. Jamie has **3** nickels. Josie has **3** dimes. Jessie has **3** quarters. If the friends share their coins, what coins would each friend have? How much money would they each have?

_____

_____

_____

25. Marta puts **12** blue tiles side by side in the bottom row. In the next row she puts **10** blue tiles above the **12** blue tiles. Then she puts **8** blue tiles above the **10** tiles. How many more rows will she need to add until there are **2** blue tiles in the top row?

_____

Subtract. (3A)

1. $4.31 $-$ 1.58	**2.** 805 $-$ 287	**3.** $7.98 $-$ 4.56	**4.** $3.02 $-$ .76

1. $4.31
    $-$ 1.58

2.   805
    $-$ 287

3. $7.98
    $-$ 4.56

4. $3.02
    $-$ .76

5.   412
    $-$ 7

6. $6.03
    $-$ 2.19

7.   854
    $-$ 582

8.   706
    $-$ 195

9. $8.92
    $-$ 5.76

10. $21.00
    $-$ 10.98

11.   722
    $-$ 453

12.   501
    $-$ 68

13.   953
    $-$ 218

14.   690
    $-$ 355

15.   1,774
    $-$ 92

16. $4.20
    $-$ .63

17.   2,400
    $-$ 386

18.   900
    $-$ 519

19.   3,100
    $-$ 287

20.   6,300
    $-$ 1,582

Estimate the difference. (3B)

21.   47 $\rightarrow$
    $-$ 31 $\rightarrow$ _____

22.   79 $\rightarrow$
    $-$ 46 $\rightarrow$ _____

23.   52 $\rightarrow$
    $-$ 13 $\rightarrow$ _____

Solve. (3C)

24. Dan has **6** pennies. Dave has **3** nickels. Derek has **3** dimes. If the friends share their coins, what coins would each friend have? How much money would they each have?

_____

_____

_____

25. Yuka puts **15** sequins side by side in the bottom row. She puts **12** sequins above the **15** sequins. Then she puts **9** sequins above the **12** sequins. How many more rows will she need to add until there are **3** sequins in the top row?

_____

Name _____

Find the products. (4A, 4B)

1. 3 × 1 = _____   **2.** 6 × 4 = _____   **3.** 4 × 2 = _____

4. 5 × 0 = _____   **5.** 5 × 3 = _____   **6.** 8 × 2 = _____

7. 3   **8.** 5   **9.** 8   **10.** 7   **11.** 1   **12.** 5
   × 3   × 6   × 4   × 3   × 5   × 8

Fill in the table. (4B, 4C)

		0	1	5	8	2	4	6	10
13.	× 3	0							
14.	× 4				32				
15.	× 5					10			

Find the product. Show the commutative property. (4B)

16. 7 × 4 = _____

_____ × _____ = _____

17. 9 × 3 = _____

_____ × _____ = _____

Complete. Show the associative property. (4B)

18. (2 × 3) × 3 = _____   or   2 × (3 × 3) = _____

_____ × _____ = _____   _____ × _____ = _____

Solve. (4D)

19. Who read the most books? How many books did he read?

_____

20. How many books did the boys read in all? How did you find the answer?

_____

_____

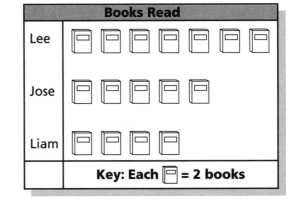

Find the products. (4A, 4B)

1. $1 \times 9 =$ _____

2. $5 \times 2 =$ _____

3. $7 \times 4 =$ _____

4. $0 \times 7 =$ _____

5. $8 \times 3 =$ _____

6. $5 \times 5 =$ _____

7. $\begin{array}{r} 4 \\ \times\,3 \\ \hline \end{array}$

8. $\begin{array}{r} 5 \\ \times\,8 \\ \hline \end{array}$

9. $\begin{array}{r} 7 \\ \times\,3 \\ \hline \end{array}$

10. $\begin{array}{r} 5 \\ \times\,4 \\ \hline \end{array}$

11. $\begin{array}{r} 6 \\ \times\,1 \\ \hline \end{array}$

12. $\begin{array}{r} 3 \\ \times\,8 \\ \hline \end{array}$

Fill in the table. (4B, 4C)

		0	1	4	6	5	9	3	10
13.	× 3	0							
14.	× 4						36		
15.	× 5						45		

Find the product. Show the commutative property. (4B)

16. $6 \times 3 =$ _____

_____ × _____ = _____

17. $8 \times 5 =$ _____

_____ × _____ = _____

Complete. Show the associative property. (4B)

18. $(2 \times 2) \times 5 =$ _____   or $2 \times (2 \times 5) =$ _____

_____ × _____ = _____   _____ × _____ = _____

Solve. (4D)

19. Which food was the favorite? How many people chose that food?

_____

20. How many people are represented in the graph? How did you find the answer?

_____

_____

Favorite Foods	
Pizza	👤👤👤👤👤
Pasta	👤👤
Burgers	👤👤👤👤👤👤👤
Fruit	👤👤👤👤
Key: Each 👤 = 2 people	

Find the quotients. (5A)

1. $8\overline{)24}$ **2.** $6\overline{)30}$ **3.** $3\overline{)15}$ **4.** $9\overline{)27}$

5. $1\overline{)5}$ **6.** $5\overline{)25}$ **7.** $4\overline{)12}$ **8.** $3\overline{)9}$

9. $7\overline{)21}$ **10.** $8\overline{)40}$ **11.** $6\overline{)24}$ **12.** $7\overline{)35}$

Find the quotients. Check by multiplication. (5B)

13. $12 \div 3 =$ _____ because _____ $\times\, 3 =$ _____

14. $18 \div 3 =$ _____ because _____ $\times\, 3 =$ _____

15. $20 \div 4 =$ _____ because _____ $\times\, 4 =$ _____

16. $12 \div 2 =$ _____ because _____ $\times\, 2 =$ _____

Write 2 multiplication sentences and 2 division sentences for this array. (5B)

17.
• • • • • •   _____ $\times$ _____ = _____   _____ $\div$ _____ = _____
• • • • • •
• • • • • •   _____ $\times$ _____ = _____   _____ $\div$ _____ = _____

Solve. (5C, 5D)

18. Stephanie bought **3** notebooks for **$9**. What was the cost of **1** notebook?

_____

19. If **6** markers cost **$12**, how much does **1** marker cost?

_____

20. Josh put **32** cans on **4** shelves. He put the same number on each shelf. How many cans were on each shelf?

_____

21. Five friends want to share **20** pencils equally. How many will each friend get?

_____

Find the quotients. (5A)

1. $8\overline{)16}$ **2.** $6\overline{)24}$ **3.** $3\overline{)18}$ **4.** $7\overline{)21}$

5. $2\overline{)4}$ **6.** $5\overline{)40}$ **7.** $4\overline{)28}$ **8.** $1\overline{)3}$

9. $7\overline{)14}$ **10.** $8\overline{)24}$ **11.** $3\overline{)21}$ **12.** $4\overline{)20}$

Find the quotients. Check by multiplication. (5B)

13. $15 \div 3 =$ _____ because _____ $\times 3 =$ _____

14. $12 \div 4 =$ _____ because _____ $\times 4 =$ _____

15. $28 \div 4 =$ _____ because _____ $\times 4 =$ _____

16. $18 \div 2 =$ _____ because _____ $\times 2 =$ _____

Write 2 multiplication sentences and 2 division sentences for this array. (5B)

17.
```
● ● ● ● ● ●
● ● ● ● ● ●
● ● ● ● ● ●
● ● ● ● ● ●
```

_____ $\times$ _____ = _____   _____ $\div$ _____ = _____

_____ $\times$ _____ = _____   _____ $\div$ _____ = _____

Solve. (5C, 5D)

18. Julia bought **3** books for **$15**. What was the cost of **1** book?

19. If **3** T-shirts cost **$24**, how much does **1** T-shirt cost?

20. Andrew put **36** stamps on **9** packages. He put the same number on each package. How many stamps were on each package?

21. Four friends want to share **28** beads equally. How many will each friend get?

Name the polygon. (6A)

1.

_____

2.

_____

3.

_____

4.

_____

5.

_____

6.

_____

Write whether the angle is a *right angle*, *greater than,* or *less than* a right angle. (6C)

7.

_____

8.

_____

9.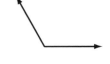

_____

Write *true* or *false.* (6A, 6C)

10. A triangle has **3** sides and is an open figure. _____

11. A rectangle is a polygon with **4** sides and **4** corners. _____

12. A square is a quadrilateral with parallel sides. _____

13. In a scalene triangle two sides are the same length. _____

14. A hexagon is an open figure with **6** sides and **6** angles. _____

15. Parallel lines are always the same distance apart. _____

Loop the figures that are congruent. (6B)

16.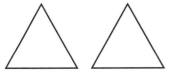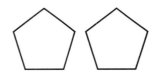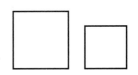

Write *equilateral, right, isosceles,* or *scalene triangle.* (6C)

17.

18.

19.

20.

_____   _____   _____   _____

Name the solid figures. Loop the ones that can roll. (6D)

21.

22.

23.

_____   _____   _____

Write whether the event is *certain, likely, unlikely,* or *impossible.* (6E)

24. You will have a birthday this year.   _____

25. One day this month will be cloudy.   _____

26. It will snow during the summer.   _____

Solve. Use the tally chart. (6F, 6G, 6H)

27. Complete the class tally chart. What is the most popular pet?

_____

Pet Survey		
Pet	Tally	Number
Dog	JHT JHT IIII	
Cat	JHT III	
Fish	IIII	

Use the line plot.

28. When the store manager orders more wood which four lengths should she probably order the least of?

_____

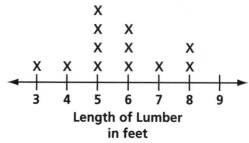

Lengths of Lumber Sold Today

Length of Lumber in feet

Name the polygon. (6A)

1.

_____

2.

_____

3.

_____

4.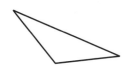

_____

5.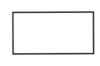

_____

6.

_____

Write whether the angle is a *right angle*, *greater than*, or *less than* a right angle. (6C)

7.

_____

8.

_____

9.

_____

Write *true* or *false*. (6A, 6C)

10. A square is a quadrilateral and is an open figure. _____

11. A right triangle is a polygon with 1 right angle. _____

12. A pentagon is a polygon with 6 sides. _____

13. A line goes on forever in two directions. _____

14. An octagon is a polygon but not a quadrilateral. _____

15. A figure can have more than one line of symmetry. _____

Loop the figures that are congruent. (6B)

16.

Write *equilateral*, *right*, *isosceles*, or *scalene triangle*. (6C)

17.   **18.**   **19.**   **20.**

_____   _____   _____   _____

Name the solid figures. Loop the ones that can roll. (6D)

21.   **22.**   **23.**

_____   _____   _____

Write whether the event is *certain*, *likely*, *unlikely*, or *impossible*. (6E)

24. There will be no full moons this year.   _____

25. A bus will be crowded during rush hour.   _____

26. You will eat some food this week.   _____

Solve. Use the tally chart. (6F, 6G, 6H)

27. Complete the class tally chart. What is the most popular color?

_____

Use the line plot.

28. Which 3 sizes of hats should the store manager order the least of for next week's sale?

_____

Favorite Color		
Color	**Tally**	**Number**
Blue	JHT IIII	
Green	JHT I	
Red	JHT JHT II	

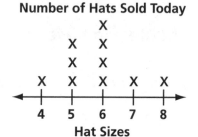

Number of Hats Sold Today

Hat Sizes

Loop the correct fraction. (7A)

1.

$\frac{1}{2}$ $\frac{2}{5}$ $\frac{2}{8}$

2.

$\frac{1}{4}$ $\frac{1}{3}$ $\frac{1}{2}$

3.

$\frac{2}{5}$ $\frac{3}{6}$ $\frac{3}{8}$

4.

$\frac{1}{2}$ $\frac{1}{3}$ $\frac{1}{4}$

What part of the figure or set is shaded? Write the fraction. (7A)

5.

_____

6.

_____

7.

_____

8.

_____

Compare. Write >, <, or =. (7B)

9.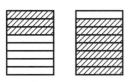

$\frac{3}{8}$ ◯ $\frac{7}{8}$

10.

$\frac{3}{5}$ ◯ $\frac{1}{5}$

11.

$\frac{3}{4}$ ◯ $\frac{3}{4}$

Order from greatest to least. (7B)

12. $\frac{3}{6}, \frac{5}{6}, \frac{1}{6},$ _____

13. $\frac{4}{7}, \frac{2}{7}, \frac{7}{7},$ _____

Write the equivalent fraction. (7C)

14.

$\frac{1}{2} = \frac{\square}{4}$

15.

$\frac{2}{3} = \frac{4}{\square}$

16.

$\frac{1}{4} = \frac{\square}{8}$

Write the number. (7G)

17.

$\frac{1}{2}$ of 8 = _____

18.

$\frac{1}{3}$ of 6 = _____

19.

$\frac{1}{4}$ of 12 = _____

Write whether the shaded part is closer to 0, $\frac{1}{2}$, or 1. (7D)

20.  _____

21. _____

Write the mixed number. (7F)

22. _____

23. _____

If there is enough information, then solve the problem. If there is not enough information, write what you need to know. (7H)

24. Amanda orders a sandwich and milk. The sandwich costs $3. She pays with a $10 bill. How much change does she get?

_____

25. Carter needs 2 cups of flour to make a loaf of bread. He has $\frac{3}{4}$ cup of whole wheat flour, 1 cup of white flour, and $\frac{1}{4}$ cup of soy flour. Does he have enough flour?

_____

26. In a bag of socks, $\frac{3}{8}$ of the pairs are blue and $\frac{5}{8}$ of the pairs are white. What fraction tells how many more pairs of white socks there are than blue? What operation did you use? Why?

_____

27. In a display of model cars, $\frac{3}{10}$ are blue, $\frac{5}{10}$ are red, and $\frac{2}{10}$ are yellow. What fraction of the models are blue or yellow?

_____

Loop the correct fraction. (7A)

1.

$\frac{1}{2}$ $\frac{1}{3}$ $\frac{1}{5}$

2.

$\frac{2}{4}$ $\frac{2}{8}$ $\frac{2}{9}$

3.

$\frac{1}{2}$ $\frac{1}{3}$ $\frac{1}{4}$

4.

$\frac{1}{5}$ $\frac{1}{6}$ $\frac{1}{7}$

What part of the figure or set is shaded? Write the fraction. (7A)

5.

_____

6.

_____

7.

_____

8.

_____

Compare. Write >, < or =. (7B)

9.

$\frac{2}{3}$ ◯ $\frac{2}{3}$

10.

$\frac{4}{6}$ ◯ $\frac{3}{6}$

11.

$\frac{1}{8}$ ◯ $\frac{2}{8}$

Order from greatest to least. (7B)

12. $\frac{2}{8}$, $\frac{7}{8}$, $\frac{5}{8}$ _____

13. $\frac{3}{4}$, $\frac{4}{4}$, $\frac{1}{4}$ _____

Write the equivalent fraction. (7C)

14.

$\frac{1}{4} = \frac{\square}{8}$

15.

$\frac{1}{2} = \frac{3}{\square}$

16.

$\frac{2}{5} = \frac{\square}{10}$

Write the number. (7G)

17.

$\dfrac{1}{2}$ of 6 = _____

18.

$\dfrac{1}{5}$ of 10 = _____

19.

$\dfrac{1}{3}$ of 12 = _____

Write whether the shaded part is closer to 0, $\dfrac{1}{2}$, or 1. (7D)

20. 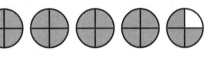 _____

21. 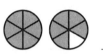 _____

Write the mixed number. (7F)

22. ⊕⊕⊕⊕⊕ _____

23. ⊗⊗ _____

....

If there is enough information, then solve the problem. If there is not enough information, write what you need to know. (7E, 7H)

24. Jason wants to buy a computer game that costs $30 and a mouse pad that costs $6. How much change will he get back?

_____

25. Emilia needs 3 cups of nuts to make some cookies. She has $\dfrac{1}{3}$ cup of pecans, 1 cup of walnuts, and $\dfrac{2}{3}$ cup of almonds. Does she have enough nuts?

_____

26. In a box of T-shirts, $\dfrac{6}{10}$ are white and $\dfrac{4}{10}$ are red. What fraction tells how many more white T-shirts there are than red? What operation did you use? Why?

_____

27. In a bowl of fruit, $\dfrac{5}{8}$ of the fruit is apples, $\dfrac{1}{8}$ of the fruit is oranges, and $\dfrac{2}{8}$ of the fruit is bananas. What fraction of the fruit is apples or bananas?

_____

Find the answer. (8A)

1. $8 \times 6 =$ _____

2. $1 \times 9 =$ _____

3. $7 \times 7 =$ _____

4. $9 \times 7 =$ _____

5. $5 \times 8 =$ _____

6. $6 \times 9 =$ _____

7.
$$\begin{array}{r} 3 \\ \times\, 9 \\ \hline \end{array}$$

8.
$$\begin{array}{r} 8 \\ \times\, 7 \\ \hline \end{array}$$

9.
$$\begin{array}{r} 8 \\ \times\, 9 \\ \hline \end{array}$$

10. $36 \div 9 =$ _____

11. $42 \div 7 =$ _____

12. $64 \div 8 =$ _____

13. $7\overline{)21}$

14. $8\overline{)40}$

15. $9\overline{)72}$

16. $6\overline{)42}$

17. $9\overline{)36}$

18. $7\overline{)56}$

Find the quotient and remainder. (8B)

19. $7\overline{)50}$

20. $8\overline{)59}$

21. $9\overline{)68}$

Complete. (8C)

22. $46 \div 7 = 6$ **R4** because (_____ $\times$ _____) + _____ = _____ .

Solve. (8B, 8D)

23. Jennie rode her bike **8** miles each day for **5** days. Write a number sentence that shows the total number of miles she rode?

_____

24. Matthew needs **6** beads to make each necklace. How many necklaces can he make from **54** beads?

_____

Find the answer. (8A)

1. $7 \times 6 =$ _____

2. $9 \times 5 =$ _____

3. $0 \times 8 =$ _____

4. $8 \times 9 =$ _____

5. $4 \times 8 =$ _____

6. $6 \times 8 =$ _____

7. $\begin{array}{r} 7 \\ \times\, 3 \\ \hline \end{array}$

8. $\begin{array}{r} 6 \\ \times\, 9 \\ \hline \end{array}$

9. $\begin{array}{r} 9 \\ \times\, 9 \\ \hline \end{array}$

10. $63 \div 9 =$ _____

11. $49 \div 7 =$ _____

12. $56 \div 8 =$ _____

13. $9\overline{)27}$

14. $6\overline{)36}$

15. $8\overline{)48}$

16. $7\overline{)42}$

17. $8\overline{)40}$

18. $9\overline{)54}$

Find the quotient and remainder. (8B)

19. $6\overline{)45}$

20. $9\overline{)48}$

21. $8\overline{)66}$

Complete. (8C)

22. $56 \div 9 = 6$ **R2** because (_____ $\times$ _____) + _____ = _____.

Solve. (8B, 8D)

23. Jamal ran **7** miles each day for **6** days. Write a number sentence that shows the total number of miles he ran.

_____

24. Maria is making a photo album. She puts **8** photos on each page. How many pages will she fill with **64** photos?

_____

Multiply. (9A)

1. 34 × 2	**2.** 23 × 3	**3.** 11 × 7	**4.** 602 × 2
5. 55 × 9	**6.** 53 × 8	**7.** 32 × 6	**8.** 504 × 5
9. 74 × 9	**10.** 86 × 5	**11.** 53 × 3	**12.** 1,432 × 2
13. 163 × 4	**14.** 319 × 8	**15.** 286 × 4	**16.** 764 × 9
17. $1.89 × 4	**18.** $2.34 × 8	**19.** $1.34 × 6	**20.** $10.49 × 8

Divide. (9B)

21. $8\overline{)98}$

22. $5\overline{)715}$

Solve. (9C)

23. Renzo wants to buy a building set for **$78**. He earns **$6** a day mowing lawns. How many days does he need to mow lawns to earn enough money?

24. Suppose you have **32** beads, $\frac{1}{2}$ are green and **9** are yellow. The rest are purple. How many purple beads do you have?

Multiply. (9A)

1. 43 × 2	**2.** 22 × 3	**3.** 11 × 9	**4.** 406 × 2
5. 76 × 9	**6.** 62 × 8	**7.** 43 × 6	**8.** 309 × 5
9. 83 × 6	**10.** 79 × 5	**11.** 59 × 3	**12.** 1,734 × 2
13. 157 × 4	**14.** 428 × 8	**15.** 359 × 4	**16.** 645 × 9
17. $1.95 × 4	**18.** $2.29 × 8	**19.** $1.42 × 6	**20.** $10.63 × 8

Divide. (9B)

21. $7\overline{)94}$

22. $4\overline{)676}$

Solve. (9C)

23. Jacqueline wants to buy a bicycle for **$92**. She earns **$6** a day delivering papers. How many days does she need to deliver papers to earn enough money?

_____

24. Suppose you have **36** marbles, $\frac{1}{2}$ are clear and **10** are white. The rest are blue. How many blue marbles do you have?

_____

Measure each segment in centimeters. (10A)

1. _____ cm

2. 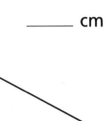 _____ cm

3.  _____ cm

Loop the better estimate. (10B, 10C, 10E)

4. weight of an egg

3 oz or **2** lb

5. height of a table

3 in. or **3** ft

6. mass of a dog

100 g or **10** kg

7. temperature of hot tea

98°C or **25°C**

8. temperature on a warm day

48°F or **89°F**

Measure each segment in inches. (10A)

9. •————————• _____ in.

10. •————————————————• _____ in.

Complete. (10D)

11. 1 pt = _____ c

12. 1 qt = _____ pt

13. 1 ft = _____ in.

14. 1 yd = _____ ft

15. 1 gal = _____ qt

16. 1 lb = _____ oz

Find the perimeter. (10F)

17.

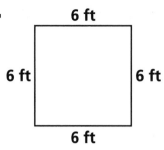

6 ft
6 ft   6 ft
6 ft

_____ ft

18.

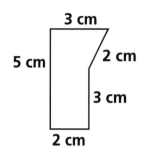

3 cm
5 cm   2 cm
3 cm
2 cm

_____ cm

19.

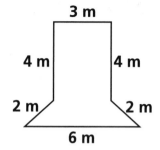

3 m
4 m   4 m
2 m   2 m
6 m

_____ m

Find the area. (10F)

20.

_____ sq units

21.

_____ sq units

22.

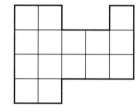

_____ sq units

Find the volume. (10F)

23.

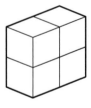

_____ cubic units

24.

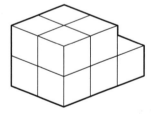

_____ cubic units

25.

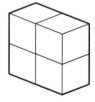

_____ cubic units

Finish the list. Solve. (10G)

26. The temperature was **20°F** at **6** A.M. It rose **5°** each hour. What is the temperature at **10** A.M.?

_____

20° at 6 A.M.

25° at 7 A.M.

_____ 8 A.M.

_____ 9 A.M.

_____ 10 A.M.

°F
— 50°
— 40°
— 30°
— 20°
— 10°
— 0°

Measure each segment in centimeters. (10A)

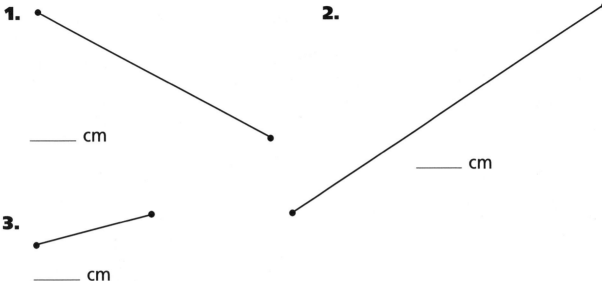

1.

_____ cm

2.

_____ cm

3.

_____ cm

Loop the better estimate. (10B, 10C, 10E)

4. weight of a chair

   5 oz or **5 lb**

5. length of a car

   8 ft or **8 mi**

6. mass of a cat

   50 g or **5 kg**

7. temperature of cold juice

   18°C or **80°C**

8. temperature of a cafeteria

   25°F or **68°F**

Measure each segment in inches. (10A)

9. •———————————•

   _____ in.

10. •——————•

   _____ in.

Complete. (10D)

11. 1 qt = _____ pt

12. 1 lb = _____ oz

13. 1 yd = _____ ft

14. 1 ft = _____ in.

15. 1 qt = _____ c

16. 1 yd = _____ in.

Find the perimeter. (10F)

17.

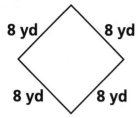

8 yd   8 yd
8 yd   8 yd

_____ yd

18.

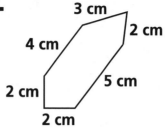

3 cm
4 cm   2 cm
2 cm   5 cm
2 cm

_____ cm

19.

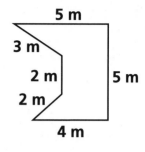

5 m
3 m
2 m   5 m
2 m
4 m

_____ m

Find the area. (10F)

20.

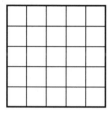

_____ sq units

21.

_____ sq units

22.

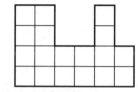

_____ sq units

Find the volume. (10F)

23.

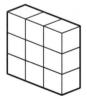

_____ cubic units

24.

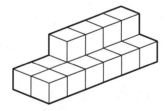

_____ cubic units

25.

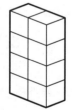

_____ cubic units

Finish the list. Solve. (10G)

26. The temperature was **10°F** at **7** A.M. It rose **10°** each hour. What is the temperature at **11** A.M.?

_____

10° at **7** A.M.	
20° at **8** A.M.	
_____ **9** A.M.	
_____ **10** A.M.	
_____ **11** A.M.	

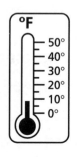

°F
50°
40°
30°
20°
10°
0°

Write the decimal. (11A, 11B)

1.

_____

2.

_____

3.

_____

4. two hundredths

_____

5. $\dfrac{53}{100}$

_____

6. four tenths

_____

Add or subtract. (11C)

7. 8.7
 + 13.3

8. 9.2
 − 4.8

9. 2.7
 + 6.9

10. 32.6
 − 14.5

Multiply or divide. (11D)

11. $2.69
 ×   8

12. $7.28
 ×   3

13. $8\overline{)\$8.48}$

14. $6\overline{)\$14.16}$

Write the part of a dollar. Use a fraction and a decimal. (11E)

15.

_____ _____

16.

_____ _____

Solve. (11F, 11G)

17. Camille wants **4** CDs that cost **$12.75** each. She has **$60**. Estimate to see if she has enough money.

_____

18. Mark has **3** quarters, **4** dimes, **1** nickel, and **2** pennies. By Saturday, he has four times that amount. How much money will he have then?

_____

Write the decimal. (11A, 11B)

1.   **2.**   **3.**

_____   _____   _____

4. five hundredths   **5.** $\dfrac{82}{100}$ **6.** nine tenths

_____   _____   _____

Add or subtract. (11C)

7.   9.4
   + 11.8

8.   8.7
   − 3.8

9.   3.6
   + 4.9

10.   29.6
   − 16.2

Multiply or divide. (11D)

11. $3.26
    ×   4

12. $9.12
    ×   5

13. $9\overline{)\$9.27}$

14. $7\overline{)\$24.15}$

Write the part of a dollar. Use a fraction and a decimal. (11E)

15.   **16.**

_____   _____   _____

Solve. (11F, 11G)

17. José wants **4** books that cost **$13.25** each. He has **$50**. Estimate to see if he has enough money.

_____

18. Gina has **2** quarters, **6** dimes, **3** nickels, and **4** pennies. By the end of the week she has five times that amount. How much money will she have then?

_____

1 Ms. Wong's art class is making a design using 18,650 tiles. What is the value of the digit 1 in the number?

A 100,000

B 10,000

C 1,000

D 100

2 Ryan has 2,048 stamps in his stamp collection. What is this number in expanded form?

F 2,000 + 400 + 80

G 2,000 + 400 + 8

H 2,000 + 40 + 8

J 200 + 40 + 8

3 Which city has the greatest population?

City	Population
Hillside	84,902
Mountainview	84,209
Oceanside	84,920
Lakeville	84,290

A Hillside

B Mountainview

C Oceanside

D Lakeville

4 The elevation of Mount Everest is twenty-nine thousand, twenty-eight feet. Which shows this number?

F 2,928

G 20,928

H 29,208

J 29,028

5 Which lists the rivers from the longest to the shortest?

River	Length (in miles)
Red	1,290
Snake	1,038
Peace	1,210
Yukon	1,979

A Yukon, Snake, Peace, Red

B Snake, Red, Peace, Yukon

C Yukon, Red, Peace, Snake

D Peace, Red, Snake, Yukon

6 Which number means 50,000 + 3,000 + 60?

F 536

G 5,360

H 53,600

J 53,060

7

Joe is tenth in line. Jill, Jody, Jim and Ja are behind Joe. Who is twelfth in line?

A Jill   **C** Jim

B Jody   **D** Ja

8 Emma has a 1 dollar bill, 2 quarters, and 2 dimes that her grandfather gave her.

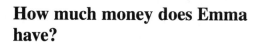

How much money does Emma have?

F $1.50   **H** $1.70

G $1.60   **J** $1.75

9 The clock shows the time that Marcia's soccer game started yesterday afternoon.

What time did the game start?

A 5:10 P.M.   **C** 5:12 P.M.

B 6:10 P.M.   **D** 6:12 P.M.

10 The movie starts at 4:15 P.M. What time will it be 12 hours after the movie starts?

F 4:15 A.M.   **H** 10:15 A.M.

G 4:15 P.M.   **J** 10:15 P.M.

11 There were 8 people on the bus. At the first stop, 3 people got off the bus and 4 more people got on. How many people were on the bus after the first stop?

A 9 people   **C** 11 people

B 12 people   **D** 15 people

12 Soup is on sale at the supermarket.

Number of Cans	Cost
2	$1
4	$2
6	$3
8	$4

How much will 12 cans of soup cost?

F $5   **H** $8

G $6   **J** $12

Assessments

13 Alissa bought a costume for $6.95 and a hat for $2.45. How much did she spend altogether?

A $8.30

B $8.40

C $9.30

D $9.40

14 Ramon has 167 baseball cards. He buys 48 more baseball cards on sale. Estimate to the nearest 10 how many baseball cards Ramon has now.

F 200 cards

G 210 cards

H 220 cards

J 230 cards

15 Gina makes a necklace with 358 beads. What is this number rounded to the nearest hundred?

A 300

B 350

C 360

D 400

16 If 4 books cost $32, how much does 1 book cost?

F $6

G $7

H $8

J $9

17 What shape is the water tank?

A cone   C sphere

B cylinder   D pyramid

18 Which term best describes the possibility of the event happening?

It will rain this spring.

F certain   H unlikely

G likely   J improbable

19 Which two figures below are congruent? Use tracing paper if needed.

A A and B

B B and C

C C and D

D A and D

20 Name the polygon used for the sign.

F quadrilateral

G pentagon

H hexagon

J octagon

Mr. Garcia's class made a pictograph of the fish in their aquariums. Use the graph to answer questions 21 and 22.

Aquarium Fish	
Angel Fish	🐟🐟
Guppy	🐟
Goldfish	🐟🐟🐟🐟
Neon	🐟🐟🐟
🐟 = 3 fish	

21 How many goldfish are in the aquariums?

A 4 goldfish

B 8 goldfish

C 12 goldfish

D 15 goldfish

22 How many more neon fish are there than guppies?

F 2

G 3

H 4

J 6

23 Which figure is *not* a quadrilateral?

A square

B rectangle

C rhombus

D hexagon

Alta School raised money for field trips by selling magazines. The bar graph shows how many magazines 4 students sold. Use the graph to answer questions 24 and 25.

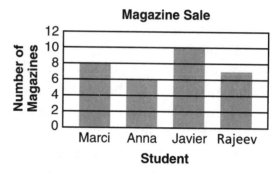

24 How many more magazines did Javier sell than Anna?

F 2 magazines

G 4 magazines

H 6 magazines

J 10 magazines

25 How many magazines did the students sell altogether?

A 21 magazines

B 24 magazines

C 26 magazines

D 31 magazines

26 Capulin Volcano National Monument is 793 acres. Muir Woods National Monument is 554 acres. About how many acres larger is Capulin Volcano?

F 100 acres   H 300 acres

G 200 acres   J 400 acres

27 There are 4 boxes of peaches. There are 6 peaches in each box. How many peaches are there altogether?

A 2 peaches   C 12 peaches

B 10 peaches   D 24 peaches

28 Which figure does *not* have a right angle?

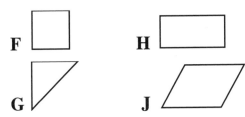

F   H

G   J

29

2,990 km

San Francisco

Chicago

New Orleans   1,341 km

A pilot flew from San Francisco to Chicago and then from Chicago to New Orleans. How many kilometers was the total trip?

A 1,649 km   C 4,231 km

B 3,231 km   D 4,331 km

30

| pencil | $.15 | ruler | $.50 |
| pen | $.45 | marker | $.30 |

Manuel spent $.75 to buy 2 different items. Which 2 items did he buy?

F pencil and ruler   H pen and marker

G pencil and pen   J ruler and marker

31 Each sticker costs 3 cents. Gish spent 15 cents. How many stickers did she buy?

A 5 stickers   C 18 stickers

B 12 stickers   D 45 stickers

32 Marcus tossed a coin 20 times. The chart shows his results. How many times did Marcus toss heads?

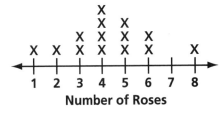

Tally	
Heads	JHT JHT II
Tails	JHT III

F 4 times   H 10 times

G 8 times   J 12 times

33 The line plot shows the number of roses in each bouquet that a florist sold. How many roses are usually in the bouquets the florist makes?

```
              X
              X   X
          X   X   X   X
  X   X   X   X   X   X           X
  |   |   |   |   |   |   |   |
  1   2   3   4   5   6   7   8
        Number of Roses
```

A 1 rose   C 4 roses

B 3 roses   D 6 roses

34 Which shows the commutative property?

F $0 \times 8 = 0$

G $1 \times 6 = 6$

H $4 \times 2 = 2 \times 4$

J $(4 \times 3) \times 2 = 4 \times (3 \times 2)$

35   386
        + 295

A 191   **C** 581   **E** NH
B 571   **D** 681

36   876
        − 98

F 974   **H** 787   **K** NH
G 822   **J** 782

37   4,010
        − 2,814

A 1,196   **C** 2,804   **E** NH
B 1,206   **D** 6,824

38 7 × 5 =

F 12   **H** 30   **K** NH
G 27   **J** 35

39 6 × 4 =

A 10   **C** 24   **E** NH
B 12   **D** 28

40   3
        × 9

F 12   **H** 24   **K** NH
G 21   **J** 27

41 8 × 10 =

A 8   **C** 80   **E** NH
B 18   **D** 180

42 4 ÷ 4 =

F 0   **H** 4   **K** NH
G 1   **J** 8

43 18 ÷ 3 =

A 5   **C** 9   **E** NH
B 6   **D** 15

44 5)‾40‾

F 6   **H** 8   **K** NH
G 7   **J** 10

1 The clock shows the time Molly eats lunch everyday. What time does she eat lunch?

A 11:15 A.M.

B 12:15 A.M.

C 11:45 A.M.

D 12:45 A.M.

2 Carlos swims on the 1st, 4th, 7th, and 10th days of the month. He will continue to swim following this pattern. On which day of the month will he *not* swim?

F 13th   H 16th

G 15th   J 19th

3 The picture on a box of plant food shows 8 flowers, each with 5 petals, and 14 flowers, each with 6 petals. How many flowers does the picture show?

A 11 flowers   C 30 flowers

B 22 flowers   D 33 flowers

4 Ivan is 3 years older than his sister. The sum of their ages is 15. How old is Ivan?

F 6   H 9

G 8   J 12

Mr. Sim's class made a pictograph to show the number of days it snowed this winter. Use the pictograph to answer questions 5 and 6.

Snow Days	
December	❄❄❄❄❄
January	❄❄❄❄❄❄❄
February	❄❄❄
❄ = 2 days	

5 How many more days did it snow in January than in February?

A 3 days

B 4 days

C 8 days

D 10 days

6 How many days did it snow from December through February?

F 15 days

G 20 days

H 26 days

J 30 days

7 Tia bought 2 notebooks that cost $3 each. She also bought a stapler for $8. There was no tax. How much change will she get from $20?

A $6   C $11

B $9   D $14

8 At a clothing store, $\frac{4}{10}$ of the shirts on a rack are blue, $\frac{5}{10}$ are white, and $\frac{1}{10}$ are red. What fraction of all the shirts are white and red?

F $\frac{1}{10}$ **H** $\frac{5}{10}$

G $\frac{4}{10}$ **J** $\frac{6}{10}$

9 The temperature at 9 A.M. was 34°F. The thermometer shows the temperature at 11 A.M. How many degrees did the temperature rise from 9 A.M. to 11 A.M.?

A 3°F   **C** 6°F

B 4°F   **D** 40°F

10 Brad has 1 quart of milk. How many cups is that?

F 2 c

G 4 c

H 6 c

J 8 c

11 Which fraction of the model is shaded?

A $\frac{2}{6}$ **C** $\frac{2}{3}$

B $\frac{4}{6}$ **D** $\frac{1}{2}$

12 About what part of the figure is shaded?

F 0   **H** $\frac{1}{2}$

G $\frac{1}{4}$ **J** 1

13 Which mixed number do the shaded parts show?

A $2\frac{1}{2}$ **C** $2\frac{5}{8}$

B $2\frac{4}{8}$ **D** $2\frac{6}{8}$

14 What decimal is the same as $\frac{4}{100}$?

F 4.0   **H** 0.4

G 0.44   **J** 0.04

15 Aaron has 12 balloons. $\frac{1}{3}$ of the balloons are silver. How many balloons is that?

A 3 balloons   **C** 6 balloons

B 4 balloons   **D** 10 balloons

16 Which fraction is equivalent to $\frac{6}{8}$?

   F $\frac{1}{4}$ **H** $\frac{2}{6}$

   G $\frac{2}{5}$ **J** $\frac{3}{4}$

17 Amy finished painting $\frac{3}{6}$ of her picture. Yumi finished painting $\frac{1}{6}$ of her picture. Tonya finished painting $\frac{4}{6}$ of her picture. Order the fractions from greatest to least.

   A $\frac{3}{6}, \frac{1}{6}, \frac{4}{6}$ **C** $\frac{4}{6}, \frac{1}{6}, \frac{3}{6}$

   B $\frac{1}{6}, \frac{3}{6}, \frac{4}{6}$ **D** $\frac{4}{6}, \frac{3}{6}, \frac{1}{6}$

18 Which is a related fact for

$$36 \div 9 = ?$$

   F $36 \div 6 = 6$ **H** $6 \times 6 = 36$

   G $9 \times 4 = 36$ **J** $36 - 9 = 27$

19 The distances from Tran's house to three friends' homes are 1.3 miles, 1.7 miles, and 0.8 miles. Order these distances from least to greatest.

   A 1.3 mi, 1.7 mi, 0.8 mi

   B 1.3 mi, 0.8 mi, 1.7 mi

   C 0.8 mi, 1.3 mi, 1.7 mi

   D 0.8 mi, 1.7 mi, 1.3 mi

20 Dave read 6 magazines each month for 8 months. What number sentence shows the total number of magazines he read?

   F $6 + 8 = 14$

   G $8 - 6 = 2$

   H $8 \times 6 = 48$

   J $8 \div 6 = 1$ R2

21 Each girl in a dance recital needs to wear 2 ankle bracelets. There are 19 bracelets. How many girls can dance in the recital?

   A 10 girls

   B 9 girls

   C 8 girls

   D 6 girls

22 Forty-eight hundredths of a tile design is colored. The rest is white. Which shows the decimal for the part that is colored?

   F 4,800   **H** 4.8

   G 48   **J** 0.48

23 $.75 is what fraction of a dollar?

   A $\frac{3}{4}$ **C** $\frac{1}{3}$

   B $\frac{1}{2}$ **D** $\frac{1}{4}$

24 Which is the best estimate for the length of the nail?

F 1 in.   H 6 in.

G 2 in.   J 1 ft

25 Which is the best estimate for the mass of an apple?

A 1 g

B 9 g

C 900 g

D 90 kg

26 Rosa's mother bought groceries that cost $18.72. She gave the cashier $20.02. How much change should she receive?

F $1.30

G $2.30

H $11.30

J $12.30

27 Leon has 1 pound of peanuts. He eats 9 ounces. How many ounces are left?

A 6 oz

B 7 oz

C 8 oz

D 10 oz

28 What is the perimeter of the figure?

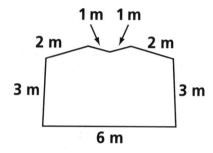

F 12 m

G 16 m

H 18 m

J 19 m

29 The school has 4 buses available for a field trip. Each bus can hold 72 students. Which is a reasonable estimate for the number of students who can go on the field trip?

A 140 students

B 200 students

C 280 students

D 320 students

30 Which amount is the greatest?

F 1 gal

G 1 qt

H 2 c

J 2 pt

31 What is the volume of the figure in cubic units? Each block is one cubic unit.

A 6 cubic units

B 9 cubic units

C 10 cubic units

D 12 cubic units

32 A baker can pack 6 muffins in a muffin box. How many boxes does he need to pack 204 muffins?

F 31 boxes

G 32 boxes

H 34 boxes

J 38 boxes

33 Clarissa baked 42 cookies each hour for 6 hours. Kevin baked 38 cookies each hour for 6 hours. How many more cookies did Clarissa bake?

A 4 cookies

B 24 cookies

C 80 cookies

D 92 cookies

Use the table to answer questions 34–36.

Item	Cost
cassette	$4.29
CD	$7.98
video	$9.50

34 What is the most reasonable estimate of the total if Sam buys 5 CDs?

F $30

G $35

H $40

J $50

35 How much will 3 cassettes cost not including tax?

A $12.27

B $12.67

C $12.77

D $12.87

36 José buys 1 of each item in the table. How much does he spend before tax?

F $20.67

G $20.77

H $21.77

J $21.78

37 Which figure cannot roll?

A

C

B

D

38 Which statement is true?

F A triangle has 3 sides and is an open figure.

G A rhombus is a quadrilateral with 4 right angles.

H A rectangle has 2 pairs of parallel sides.

J A hexagon has 5 sides and 6 angles.

39 Kimberly takes a tile from a bag without looking. The bag is filled with the following tiles.

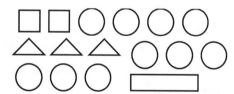

Which tile will she most likely draw from the bag?

A square

B circle

C triangle

D rectangle

40 What number will make this number sentence true?

$$8 \times 6 = \boxed{} \times 8$$

F 8

G 6

H 14

J 48

41 Which is the best estimate for the capacity of a car's gas tank?

A 15 c

B 15 pt

C 15 qt

D 15 gal

42 Leo has 95 marbles. He puts 8 marbles in each bag. How many bags does Leo need if he wants to put all the marbles in bags?

F 8 bags

G 10 bags

H 11 bags

J 12 bags

43
    21
  839
+ 67

A 917   C 927   E NH

B 926   D 937

44
  6,827
− 4,299

F 2,672

G 10,016

H 10,127

J 11,126

K NH

45
  $86.95
+ 19.87

A $67.08

B $95.72

C $105.82

D $106.82

E NH

46
  90
− 18

F 78   H 88   K NH

G 82   J 108

47
  600
− 215

A 385   C 415   E NH

B 395   D 815

48
  3,819
− 2,985

F 834

G 934

H 1,174

J 6,804

K NH

49
  7
× 4

A 11   C 24   E NH

B 22   D 28

50 40 ÷ 8 =

F 4   H 10   K NH

G 5   J 32

51 9 × 6 =

A 45   C 56   E NH

B 54   D 63

52 8)‾56‾

F 6 R2

G 7

H 7 R4

J 8

K NH

53 65 ÷ 9 =

A 6 R2

B 6 R8

C 7 R2

D 8RI

E NH

54 $\frac{1}{3} + \frac{1}{3} =$

F $\frac{1}{9}$ H $\frac{3}{6}$ K NH

G $\frac{2}{6}$ J $\frac{2}{3}$

55 $\frac{9}{10} - \frac{5}{10} =$

A $\frac{4}{5}$ C $\frac{4}{10}$ E NH

B $\frac{4}{9}$ D $\frac{5}{10}$

56 72 × 8 =

F 9   H 566   K NH

G 80   J 576

57 $\frac{1}{6}$ of 18 =

A 2   C 6   E NH

B 3   D 12

58
$$\begin{array}{r} 561 \\ \times \quad 9 \\ \hline \end{array}$$

F 570   H 4,549   K NH

G 4,449   J 5,049

59
$$\begin{array}{r} \$3.24 \\ \times \quad 8 \\ \hline \end{array}$$

A $25.92

B $25.62

C $24.62

D $24.32

E NH

60 3)‾87

F 27   H 29   K NH

G 28   J 90

61 4)‾$4.32

A $1.04

B $1.08

C $1.40

D $1.80

E NH

62 6)‾326

F 53   H 54 R2   K NH

G 53 R2   J 54 R3

Reteach Worksheets

NOTES

When the minute hand points to **12** on a clock and the hour hand points to a number, the time is given by the hour hand. Remember that the minute hand is longer than the hour hand.

Tell the time.

minute hand

Tell the time.

`10:00`

| The hour hand points to **10.** | The time is 10:00. |

| Time can also be shown on a digital clock. | Read the time shown in the display: 10:00. |

Elapsed time is the amount of time that goes by. What time will it be in one hour?

| The hour hand is pointing to **7.** | The time now is 7:00. | In one hour the time will be 8:00. |

Match the clocks that show the same time.

1.

_____

2.

_____

a. `3:00`

b.  `2:00`

c. `11:00`

3.

_____

4.

_____

d. `9:00`

5. Look at the clock in Exercise **4.** What time will it be in **1** hour? _____

Teacher Note: Use before Unit 1, Lesson 1. **(3)**

Use the symbols < and > to compare
numbers.

> | < means *is less than*
> | > means *is greater than*

Compare 5,603 and 5,630.

Use a place-value chart to help. Compare the numbers
in each column. Start at the left because the number
at the left has the greatest place value.

Thousands	Hundreds	Tens	Ones
5	6	0	3
5	6	3	0

> The thousands are the same.

> The hundreds are the same.

> Stop. The tens are different. 0 < 3

So, **5,603 < 5,630.**

Order 715, 751, 571, and 517 from least to greatest.

> The least number is **517.**

> 571 < 715, so it is next.

> 715 < 751, so it is after **571.**

The greatest number is **751.**

So, the correct order from least to greatest is **517, 571, 715, 751.**

Write the numbers in the chart. Then write > or <.

1. 248 ◯ 243

H	T	O

2. 162 ◯ 99

H	T	O

3. 6,273 ◯ 6,373

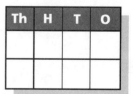

Th	H	T	O

Order the numbers from least to greatest.

4. 78, 87, 107, 88

5. 432, 423, 443, 234

6. 654, 554, 655, 456

7. 3,589; 3,895; 3,559; 3,598

Teacher Note: Use before Unit 1, Lesson 1. **(3)**

Write the number for these models.

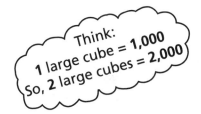

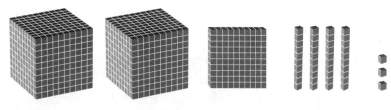

Thousands	Hundreds	Tens	Ones
2	1	4	3

Standard Form: **2,143**

Put a comma after the thousands place to make the number easier to read.

Read as two thousand, one hundred forty-three.

Expanded Form: **2,000 + 100 + 40 + 3** or
                   2 thousands 1 hundred 4 tens 3 ones

Word Form: two thousand, one hundred forty-three

Write the number.

1.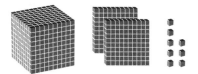

_____

2.

_____

3.

Thousands	Hundreds	Tens	Ones
6	8	5	2

_____

4.

Thousands	Hundreds	Tens	Ones
4	5	3	7

_____

5. 7,000 + 200 + 10 _____

6. 5,000 + 900 + 70 + 9 _____

7. 3,000 + 60 + 2 _____

8. 4,000 + 500 + 8 _____

9. 2 thousands 1 hundred 7 tens 3 ones

_____

10. 6 thousands 6 hundreds 2 tens 4 ones

_____

Teacher Note: Use after Quick Check, page 8, to reteach Unit 1, Lesson 1. (3)

The place-value chart shows the number **651,732**.
To write the number in expanded form, think about
the value of each digit.

Hundred Thousands	Ten Thousands	Thousands	Hundreds	Tens	Ones
6	5	1	7	3	2

A **6** in the hundred thousands place means **600,000**.

A **5** in the ten thousands place means **50,000**.

A **1** in the one thousands place means **1,000**.

A **7** in the hundreds place
means **700**.

A **3** in the tens
place means **30**.

A **2** in
the ones
place
means **2**.

600,000 + 50,000 + 1,000 + 700 + 30 + 2 = 651,732

Write each number in expanded form.

1. 187,029

100,000 + 80,000 + _____

2. 62,107

_____

3. 67,421

_____

Write the value of the digit in the number 958,072.

4. 9 _____   **5.** 5 _____   **6.** 8 _____

7. 0 _____   **8.** 7 _____   **9.** 2 _____

Teacher Note: Use after Quick Check, page 8, to reteach Unit 1, Lesson 2. **(3)**

Compare **214,375** and **214,405** using a place-value chart. Compare each place from left to right.

Thousands			Ones		
Hundreds	Tens	Ones	Hundreds	Tens	Ones
2	1	4	3	7	5
2	1	4	4	0	5

The hundred thousands are the same.

The ten thousands are the same.

The thousands are the same.

3 hundreds are less than **4** hundreds.

So, **214,375 < 214,405**

Write the numbers in the chart. Then write > , <, or = .

1. 316 ◯ 309

H	T	O
3	1	6
3	0	9

2. 4,870 ◯ 985

Th	H	T	O
4	8	7	0

3. 12,349 ◯ 12,086

TTh	Th	H	T	O

4. 45,117 ◯ 45,120

TTh	Th	H	T	O

5. 87,004 ◯ 82,008

TTh	Th	H	T	O

6. 519,326 ◯ 519,526

HTh	TTh	Th	H	T	O

Teacher Note: Use after Quick Check, page 8, to reteach Unit 1, Lesson 3. **(3)**

Use a dollar sign ($) and a decimal point (.) to write the value.

Dollars	Dimes	Pennies
5	3	7

Count how many bills: **5.** So the value of the dollars is **$5.00.** > Count how many dimes: **3.** So the value of the dimes is **$.30.** > Count how many pennies: **7.** So the value of the pennies is **$.07.** > The total value of the money shown is **$5.37.**

Complete the chart. Give the value. Use a ($) and (.).

1.

Dollars	Dimes	Pennies
3	4	

$ _____ . _____

2.

Dollars	Dimes	Pennies
2		

$ _____ . _____

3.

Dollars	Dimes	Pennies

_____

4.

Dollars	Dimes	Pennies

_____

Teacher Note: Use after Quick Check, page 18, to reteach Unit 1, Lesson 4. **(3)**

| penny 1¢ | nickel 5¢ | dime 10¢ | quarter 25¢ | half-dollar 50¢ |

Complete: 1 dime and 3 nickels = 1 _____

Start with the value of the dime because it is the coin with the greatest value. **10¢** ⟩ Count by **5's** for each nickel to find the value: **10¢, 15¢, 20¢, 25¢.** ⟩ A quarter also has a value of **25¢.** ⟩ 1 dime and 3 nickels = 1 quarter or **25¢.**

Write an equal amount using other coins. Then write the value.

1. 2 nickels = 1 ___dime___

_____ ¢

2. 2 dimes and 1 nickel = 1 ____

_____ ¢

3. 5 nickels = 1 _____

_____ ¢

4. 2 quarters = 1 _____

_____ ¢

5. 5 dimes = 1 _____

_____ ¢

6. 5 pennies = 1 _____

_____ ¢

Name _____

Write the amount.

Think: To find the amount, you must count the money.
Use the value of each bill or coin to count the money.

| Start with the dollar bill since it has the greatest value. | Count the coins in order from greatest value to least value. **$1.00, $1.25, $1.50, $1.55, $1.56, $1.57.** | The amount is **$1.57.** |

Write each amount of money.

1.

$ _____ . _____

2.

$ _____ . _____

3.

_____

4.

_____

5.

_____

6.

_____

Teacher Note: Use after Quick Check, page 18, to reteach Unit 1, Lesson 7. **(3)**

Natalie has **50¢**. She spends **33¢**. Draw the fewest coins she could get in change. Write the amount.

Use the value of pennies, nickels, and dimes to help you find the fewest coins. Think: To find the change, you count up from **33**. Stop when you reach **50**. You can count by **1's, 5's,** or **10's.**

Count up by **1** from **33¢** to **34¢** so draw a penny.	Count by **1** to **35** so draw another penny.	Count by **5** from **35¢** to **40¢,** so draw a nickel.	Count by **10** from **40¢** to **50¢.** Draw a dime to show **10¢.**
34¢	**35¢**	**40¢**	**50¢**

Natalie's change is **17¢.**

How much change? Draw to show the change using the fewest coins.

1. Brittany has **a quarter** or **25¢.** She spends **20¢.**

_____

2. Matthew has **3 dimes** or **30¢.** He spends **24¢.**

_____

3. Jamal has a **half-dollar** or **50¢.** He spends **24¢.**

_____

4. Luisa has **5 nickels** or **25¢.** She spends **15¢.**

_____

5. Heather has **2 nickels** or **10¢.** She spends **7¢.**

_____

6. Jake has **4 dimes** or **40¢.** He spends **29¢.**

_____

Teacher Note: Use after Quick Check, page 26, to reteach Unit 1, Lesson 8. **(3)**

Ordinal numbers show order or position. The table
below gives some ordinal numbers.

first 1st	second 2nd	third 3rd	fourth 4th	fifth 5th	sixth 6th	seventh 7th	eighth 8th	ninth 9th	tenth 10th

November

Sunday	Monday	Tuesday	Wednesday	Thursday	Friday	Saturday
					1	2
3	4	5	6	7	8	9
10	11	12	13	14	15	16
17	18	19	20	21	22	23
24	25	26	27	28	29	30

Use the calendar. Write the day of the week.

1. the first day of November

_____

2. the **7th** day of November

_____

3. the **18th** day of November

_____

4. the **30th** day of November

_____

Use an ordinal number to write the date.

5. the first Sunday in
November

_____

6. the second Friday in
November

_____

7. What is the **6th** letter in the word

November? _____

8. Sunday is the first day of the week.

What is the **5th** day of the week? _____

Teacher Note: Use after Quick Check, page 26, to reteach Unit 1, Lesson 10. **(3)**

When telling time, remember that the minute hand is longer than the hour hand. It takes **5** minutes for the minute hand to move from one number to the next.

Tell the time.  To find the minutes, count forward by **5's.**

The hour hand is between **7** and **8**. Read the hour as **7.**	Start at **12**. Count by **5's.** Stop where the minute hand points at **3.**	Think: **"5, 10, 15."** The number of minutes after the hour is **15.**

The time is **15** minutes after **7**, or **7:15**.

When the minute hand points to a mark past the **6**, time is often given in minutes to the next hour.

Tell the time.  To find the minutes, count back by **5's.**

The hour hand is between the **3** and the **4**. The next hour will be **"4."**	Start at **12**. Count back by **5's.** Stop where the minute hand points at **8.**	Think: **"5, 10, 15, 20."** The number of minutes to the hour is **20.**

The time is **20** minutes to **4**, or **3:40**.

Write the time in two ways.

1.

10 minutes after 5

or _____

2.

5 minutes after _____

or _____

3.

15 minutes to 11

or _____

Teacher Note: Use after Quick Check, page 26, to reteach Unit 1, Lesson 11. (3)

It takes **1** minute for the minute hand to move from one mark to the next mark.

Tell the time.

The hour hand is between the **1** and the **2**. Read the hour as **1**. > Start at **12**. Count by **5's**. Stop at the number before the minute hand. Think: **5, 10, 15**. > Count by ones, starting after **15**. Stop where the minute hand is pointing. Think: **16, 17, 18**.

The time is **18 minutes after 1**, or **1:18**.

Write the time in two ways.

1.

8 minutes after **10**

or _____

2.

23 minutes after _____

or _____

3.

18 minutes to **7**

or _____

4.

7 minutes to _____

or _____

Teacher Note: Use after Quick Check, page 30, to reteach Unit 1, Lesson 12. **(3)**

The clock shows the time Jeff jogs every morning. What time does Jeff jog?

Think: Midnight is **12:00** A.M.

The time from midnight to noon is A.M. time.

Jeff jogs at **7:15** A.M.

Lyta walks her dog every afternoon at the same time. What time does Lyta walk her dog?

Think: Noon is **12:00** P.M.

The time from noon to midnight is P.M. time.

Lyta walks her dog at **4:30** P.M.

Write the correct time for each activity. Write A.M. or P.M. to show whether it is before noon or after noon.

1. Jacob eats a late lunch.

2. Marta has a dance class on Saturday mornings.

3. Renzo has soccer practice after school.

4. Sable goes to the library before lunch.

5. Carlos wakes up for school.

6. Julia goes to a movie after school.

Teacher Note: Use after Quick Check, page 30, to reteach Unit 1, Lesson 13. (3)

Round **76** to the nearest ten.

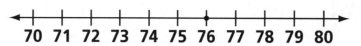

| Use a number line. | Mark **76** on the number line. | **76** is closer to **80** than to **70**. | **76** rounds up to **80**. |

Round **328** to the nearest hundred.

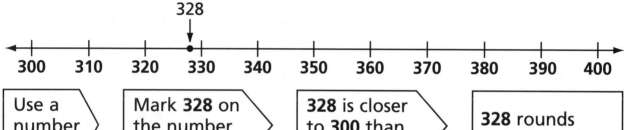

| Use a number line. | Mark **328** on the number line. | **328** is closer to **300** than to **400**. | **328** rounds down to **300**. |

Mark the number on the number line.
Then round the number to the nearest ten.

1.

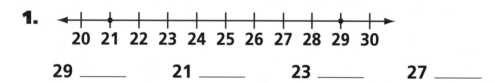

29 _____   21 _____   23 _____   27 _____

2.

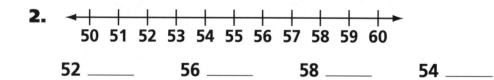

52 _____   56 _____   58 _____   54 _____

Mark the number on the number line.
Then round the number to the nearest hundred.

3.

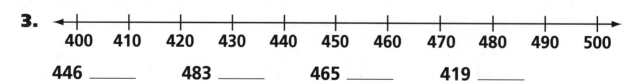

446 _____   483 _____   465 _____   419 _____

4.

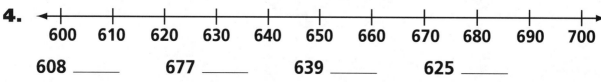

608 _____   677 _____   639 _____   625 _____

Teacher Note: Use after Quick Check, page 50, to reteach Unit 2, Lesson 7. **(3)**

Round **6,458** to the nearest thousand.

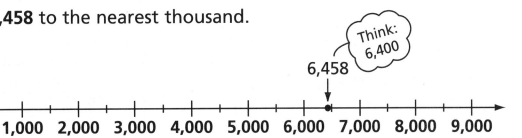

Think: 6,400

6,458

| Use a number line. | Use the hundreds digit to locate and mark **6,458** on the number line. | **6,458** is closer to **6,000** than to **7,000**. | **6,458** rounds down to **6,000**. |

Mark the number on the number line. Then round the number to the nearest thousand.

1.

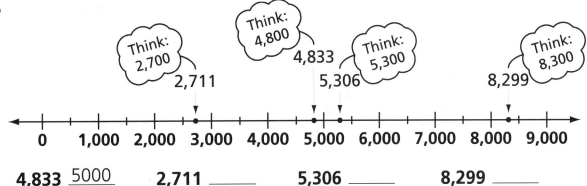

Think: 2,700

Think: 4,800

Think: 5,300

Think: 8,300

2,711   4,833   5,306   8,299

4,833 _5000_   **2,711** _____   **5,306** _____   **8,299** _____

2.

4,872   7,438

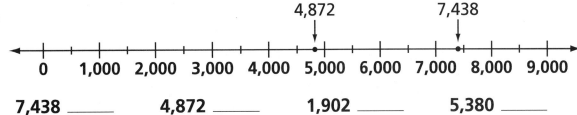

7,438 _____   **4,872** _____   **1,902** _____   **5,380** _____

3.

0 1,000 2,000 3,000 4,000 5,000 6,000 7,000 8,000 9,000

5,096 _____   **2,195** _____   **7,852** _____   **4,009** _____

Estimate the sum.   38
                        + 65

| Round each number to the nearest ten. | 38 rounds to **40**. 65 rounds to **70**. (Remember: When the ones digit is **5** or greater, round up to the next ten.) | Add the rounded numbers. 38 → 40 + 65 → + 70 —————— 110 ← estimated sum |

Round each number to the nearest ten.
Estimate the sum.

1. 53 → 50
     + 26 → + 30
     —————
          80

2. 81 → 80
     + 34 → + 30

3. 94 → 90
     + 77 → + 80

4. 29 →
     + 42 → + ____

5. 58 →
     + 55 → + ____

6. 36 →
     + 89 → + ____

7. 11 →
     + 56 → + ____

8. 73 →
     + 92 → + ____

9. 75 →
     + 38 → + ____

10. 29 →
      + 42 → + ____

11.   8 →
      + 55 → + ____

12. 27 →
      + 89 → + ____

13. 33 →
      + 12 → + ____

14. 51 →
      + 19 → + ____

15. 46 →
      + 24 → + ____

Teacher Note: Use after Quick Check, page 54, to reteach Unit 2, Lesson 9. **(3)**

You add money the same way that you add
whole numbers. Just remember to
line up the dollars and the cents.

Add. $6.37
     + 1.09

Dollars	.	Dimes	Pennies
$ 6	.	3	7
+ 1	.	0	9

```
      1
$ 6 . 3 7
+ 1 . 0 9
        6
```
Add the
pennies.
Regroup.

```
      1
$ 6 . 3 7
+ 1 . 0 9
      4 6
```
Add the
dimes. No
regrouping
is needed.

```
      1
$ 6 . 3 7
+ 1 . 0 9
  7 4 6
```
Add the
dollars.

```
      1
$ 6 . 3 7
+ 1 . 0 9
$ 7 . 4 6
```
Write the $
and . in the
answer.

Add.

1.
```
    1
$ 5 . 4 1
+   . 7 2
      1 3
```

2.
```
  1   1
$ 3 . 9 9
+ 2 . 5 3
    . 5 2
```

3.
```
        1
$ 2 . 6 5
+ 1 . 2 8
    .   3
```

4.
```
$ 2 . 5 5
+ 3 . 6 8
```

5.
```
$ 1 . 0 4
+ 1 . 7 2
```

6.
```
$ 6 . 1 9
+ 2 . 8 3
```

7.
```
$ 5 . 7 2
+   . 9 6
```

8.
```
$ 4 . 3 9
+   . 0 5
```

9.
```
$ 5 . 2 4
+ 3 . 1 7
```

10. $2.61
       + 4.86

11. $1.45
       + 5.17

12. $1.69
       + 7.08

When subtracting from hundreds, you may have to regroup a ten or a hundred or both.

Subtract: **800 − 364.**

H	T	O
8	0	0
− 3	6	4

Since **0 < 4**, you cannot subtract the ones. Regroup a ten.

H	T	O
	7	10
8	0	0
− 3	6	4

There are no tens. So regroup a hundred as **10 tens.**

H	T	O
		9
7	10	10
8	0	0
− 3	6	4

Then regroup a ten as **10 ones.** There are **9 tens** left.

H	T	O
	9	
7	10	10
8	0	0
− 3	6	4
		6

Subtract the ones.

H	T	O
	9	
7	10	10
8	0	0
− 3	6	4
	3	6

Subtract the tens.

H	T	O
	9	
7	10	10
8	0	0
− 3	6	4
4	3	6

Subtract the hundreds. The difference is **436.**

Subtract.

1.
H	T	O
4	9/10	10
5	0	0
− 2	1	9

2.
H	T	O
	9/10	10
3	0	0
−	8	7

3.
H	T	O
	9/10	10
6	0	0
− 2	4	8

4.
H	T	O
		10
9	0	0
− 6	5	2

5. 400
  − 274

6. 200
  − 116

7. 700
  − 383

8. 800
  − 485

Teacher Note: Use after Quick Check, page 76, to reteach Unit 3, Lesson 5. **(3)**

You subtract money the same way that you subtract whole numbers. Just remember to regroup when necessary and to line up the dollars and the cents.

Subtract. **$6.37**
− 1.59

Dollars	.	Dimes	Pennies
6	.	3	7
1	.	5	9

$ +

			2	17
$ 6	.	3̸	7̸	
− 1	.	5	9	
			8	

Regroup to subtract the pennies.

	5	12	17
$ 6̸	.	3̸	7̸
− 1	.	5	9
		7	8

Regroup to subtract the dimes.

	5	12	17
$ 6̸	.	3̸	7̸
− 1	.	5	9
4		7	8

Subtract the dollars.

	5	12	17
$ 6̸	.	3̸	7̸
− 1	.	5	9
$ 4	.	7	8

Write the $ and . in the answer.

Subtract.

1.
	4		15	
$ 5̸	.	5̸	6	2
−	.		7	2
	.		8	4

2.
		8	10	
$ 3	.	0̸	0	3
− 1	.	2		3
	.		6	7

3.
		5	10	
$ 2	.	6̸	5̸	8
− 1	.	2		8
	.			7

4.
$ 5	.	7	9	8
− 1	.	6		8
	.			

5.
$ 4	.	2	3	2
− 1	.	7		2
	.			

6.
$ 6	.	0	5	3
− 2	.	8		3
	.			

7.
$ 5	.	7	2	6
− 2	.	9		6
	.			

8.
$ 4	.	2	9	5
− 1	.	9		5
	.			

9.
$ 5	.	0	0	7
− 3	.	1		7
	.			

10. $4.01
      − 1.86

11. $6.45
      − 5.17

12. $7.62
      − 3.08

Teacher Note: Use after Quick Check, page 76, to reteach Unit 3, Lesson 6. **(3)**

Estimate the difference.   **82**
                          − 35

| Round each number to the nearest ten. | 82 rounds to 80. 35 rounds to 40. (Remember, when the ones digit is 5 or greater, round up to the next ten.) | Subtract the rounded numbers. $$\begin{array}{r} 82 \rightarrow 80 \\ -35 \rightarrow -40 \\ \hline 40 \end{array}$$ ← estimated difference |

Round each number to the nearest ten.
Estimate the difference.

1. $\begin{array}{r} 54 \rightarrow 50 \\ -26 \rightarrow -30 \\ \hline 20 \end{array}$

2. $\begin{array}{r} 81 \rightarrow 80 \\ -32 \rightarrow -30 \\ \hline \end{array}$

3. $\begin{array}{r} 74 \rightarrow 70 \\ -17 \rightarrow -20 \\ \hline \end{array}$

4. $\begin{array}{r} 89 \rightarrow \\ -42 \rightarrow - \\ \hline \end{array}$

5. $\begin{array}{r} 68 \rightarrow \\ -25 \rightarrow - \\ \hline \end{array}$

6. $\begin{array}{r} 89 \rightarrow \\ -26 \rightarrow - \\ \hline \end{array}$

7. $\begin{array}{r} 51 \rightarrow \\ -36 \rightarrow - \\ \hline \end{array}$

8. $\begin{array}{r} 91 \rightarrow \\ -32 \rightarrow - \\ \hline \end{array}$

9. $\begin{array}{r} 75 \rightarrow \\ -38 \rightarrow - \\ \hline \end{array}$

10. $\begin{array}{r} 79 \rightarrow \\ -47 \rightarrow - \\ \hline \end{array}$

11. $\begin{array}{r} 88 \rightarrow \\ -55 \rightarrow - \\ \hline \end{array}$

12. $\begin{array}{r} 67 \rightarrow \\ -19 \rightarrow - \\ \hline \end{array}$

13. $\begin{array}{r} 33 \rightarrow \\ -12 \rightarrow - \\ \hline \end{array}$

14. $\begin{array}{r} 71 \rightarrow \\ -29 \rightarrow - \\ \hline \end{array}$

15. $\begin{array}{r} 66 \rightarrow \\ -24 \rightarrow - \\ \hline \end{array}$

Teacher Note: Use after Quick Check, page 82, to reteach Unit 3, Lesson 8. **(3)**

You can use groups to skip-count. Count by **2's**.

         9 groups of 2

2,   4,   6,   8,   10,   12,   14,   16,   18   18 in all

1. Skip-count by **2's**. Write how many groups of **2** and how many in all.

_____ groups of 2

_____, _____, _____, _____, _____, _____   _____ in all

2. Skip-count by **3's**. Write how many groups of **3** and how many in all.

_____ groups of 3

3,   6,   9,   12, _____, _____, _____   _____ in all

3. Skip-count by **4's**. Complete.

_____ groups of 4

4,   8,   12, _____, _____, _____, _____   _____ in all

4. Skip count by **5's**. Complete.

_____ groups of 5

5, _____, _____, _____, _____, _____, _____   _____ in all

5. Skip count by **10's**. Complete.

_____ groups of 10

10,   20, _____, _____   _____ in all

Teacher Note: Use before Unit 4, Lesson 1. **(3)**

Here is an **array** of dots.
It has **3** rows of **2** dots.
There are **6** dots in all.

3 rows of **2** dots

$3 \times 2 = 6$

You can turn the array to show **2** rows
of **3** dots. It still has **6** dots in all.

2 rows of **3** dots

$2 \times 3 = 6$

Complete.

1.

2 rows of _____ dots

$2 \times 4 = 8$

Turn the array. Draw it.

_____ rows of _____ dots

$4 \times 2 =$ _____

2.

4 rows of _____ dots

$4 \times 3 = 12$

Turn the array. Draw it.

_____ rows of _____ dots

$3 \times 4 =$ _____

3.

3 rows of _____ dots

$3 \times 5 =$ _____

Turn the array. Draw it.

_____ rows of _____ dots

_____ × _____ = _____

4.

2 rows of _____ dots

$2 \times 5 =$ _____

Turn the array. Draw it.

_____ rows of _____ dots

_____ × _____ = _____

Teacher Note: Use before Unit 4, Lesson 1. **(3)**

The picture shows **5** groups of **2**.

You can write an addition sentence and a multiplication sentence to describe the groups.

$2 + 2 + 2 + 2 + 2 = 10$

$5 \times 2 = 10$

Complete the number sentences.

1.

$2 + 2 + 2 =$ _____

$3 \times 2 =$ _____

2.

$2 + 2 + 2 + 2 =$ _____

$4 \times 2 =$ _____

3.

$2 + 2 + 2 + 2 + 2 + 2 =$ _____

_____ $\times 2 =$ _____

4.

$2 + 2 =$ _____

_____ $\times 2 =$ _____

5.

$2 + 2 + 2 + 2 + 2 + 2 + 2 =$ _____

_____ $\times$ _____ $=$ _____

6.

$2 + 2 + 2 + 2 + 2 + 2 + 2 + 2 + 2 =$ _____

_____ $\times$ _____ $=$ _____

7.

$2 + 2 + 2 + 2 + 2 + 2 + 2 + 2 =$ _____

_____ $\times$ _____ $=$ _____

Teacher Note: Use after Quick Check, page 94, to reteach Unit 4, Lesson 1. **(3)**

Find the product: **4 × 2**.

You can draw **4** groups of **2**.	You can draw an array of **4** rows of **2**.	You can draw a number line.
	• • • • • • • •	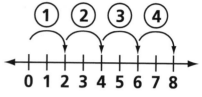
4 groups of **2**	**4** rows of **2**	**4 × 2 = 8**
2 + 2 + 2 + 2 = 8	**4 × 2 = 8**	
4 × 2 = 8		

Write the product.

1. 2 × 6 = _____

2. 3 × 2 = _____

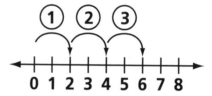

3. 2 × 8 = _____

4. 2 × 7 = _____

• • • • • • •
• • • • • • •

5. 2 × 2 = _____

Think: **2** groups of **2**

6. 5 × 2 = _____

Think: **5** groups of **2**

7. 1 × 2 = _____

8. 0 × 2 = _____

Write the product.

9. 7 × 2 = _____

10. 4 × 2 = _____

11. 2 × 8 = _____

12. 5 × 2 = _____

13. 0 × 2 = _____

14. 2 × 3 = _____

15. 1 × 2 = _____

16. 2 × 6 = _____

17. 8 × 2 = _____

18. 5 × 2 = _____

19. 9 × 2 = _____

20. 2 × 7 = _____

Teacher Note: Use after Quick Check, page 94, to reteach Unit 4, Lesson 2. **(3)**

You know that **4 + 6** equals **6 + 4**. This same property works for multiplication.

```
•  •        •  •  •
•  •        •  •  •
•  •
```

3 × 2 = 6   **2 × 3 = 6**

The **order** of the factors is different, but the product is still the same.

This is the Commutative Property of Multiplication.

You know that **(3 + 1) + 5** equals **3 + (1 + 5)**. This same property works for multiplication.

(2 × 1) × 3 = 6

2 × (1 × 3) = 6

The **grouping** of the factors is different, but the product is still the same.

This is the Associative Property of Multiplication.

Find the products. Then show the commutative property of multiplication.

1.

4 × 2 = _____

2 × 4 = _____

2.

5 × 2 = _____

2 × 5 = _____

3. 8 × 2 = _____   2 × 8 = _____

4. 1 × 2 = _____   2 × 1 = _____

5. 6 × 2 = _____

2 × _____ = _____

6. 9 × 2 = _____

2 × _____ = _____

7. 0 × 2 = _____

_____ × _____ = _____

8. 7 × 2 = _____

_____ × _____ = _____

Complete. Always work within the parentheses first.

9. (4 × 2) × 1 = ▨

8 × 1 = _____

or

4 × (2 × 1) = ▨

4 × 2 = _____

10. (6 × 1) × 2 = ▨

6 × 2 = _____

or

6 × (1 × 2) = ▨

6 × _____ = _____

11. (5 × 2) × 1 = ▨

_____ × 1 = _____

or

5 × (2 × 1) = ▨

5 × _____ = _____

Teacher Note: Use after Quick Check, page 94, to reteach Unit 4, Lesson 3. (3)   **83**

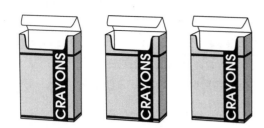
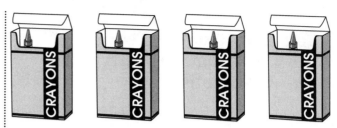

3 crayon boxes
0 crayons in each box

Think:

$$0 + 0 + 0 \rightarrow 3 \times 0 = 0$$

There are **0** crayons in all.

Any number times **0** is **0**.

0 times any number is **0**.

4 crayon boxes
1 crayon in each box

Think:

$$1 + 1 + 1 + 1 \rightarrow 4 \times 1 = 4$$

There are **4** crayons in all.

Any number times **1** is that number.

1 times any number is that number.

Write the product.

1. $1 + 1 + 1 = 3 \times 1 = $ _____

2. $1 + 1 = 1 \times 2 = $ _____

3. $1 + 1 + 1 + 1 = 4 \times 1 = $ _____

4. $5 \times 1 = $ _____

5. $8 \times 1 = $ _____

6. $1 \times 9 = $ _____

7. $0 + 0 = 2 \times 0 = $ _____

8. $0 + 0 + 0 = 3 \times 0 = $ _____

9. $0 \times 6 = $ _____

10. $7 \times 0 = $ _____

11. $0 \times 3 = $ _____

12. $1 \times 0 = $ _____

13. $2 \times 1 = $ _____

14. $1 \times 8 = $ _____

15. $0 \times 9 = $ _____

16. $9 \times 1 = $ _____

Write the product or missing factor.

17. $6 \times $ _____ $= 6$

18. _____ $\times 4 = 4$

19. $1 \times 8 = $ _____

20. $0 \times 7 = $ _____

21. _____ $\times 1 = 7$

22. _____ $\times 3 = 0$

23. $9 \times 0 = $ _____

24. $0 \times 2 = $ _____

25. $1 \times $ _____ $= 5$

26. $6 \times $ _____ $= 0$

Teacher Note: Use after Quick Check, page 102, to reteach Unit 4, Lesson 4. **(3)**

Find **4 × 5.**

Think: **4 groups of 5**

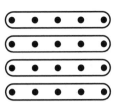

$$5 + 5 + 5 + 5 \rightarrow 4 \times 5 = 20$$

You can also skip-count by fives to help you multiply with **5.** In the chart, the shaded boxes show counting by fives.

Count the first **4** shaded boxes: **5, 10, 15, 20.**

So **4 × 5 = 20.**

1	2	3	4	5	6	7	8	9	10	11	12	13	14	15
16	17	18	19	20	21	22	23	24	25	26	27	28	29	30
31	32	33	34	35	36	37	38	39	40	41	42	43	44	45

Find the product.

1. $2 \times 5 =$ _____

Think: **2** groups of **5** or count **2** shaded boxes.

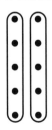

2. $5 \times 5 =$ _____

Think: **5** groups of **5** or count **5** shaded boxes.

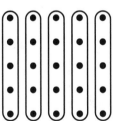

3. $5 \times 3 =$ _____

Think: **5** groups of **3.**

4. $5 \times 1 =$ _____

Think: **5** groups of **1.**

5. $6 \times 5 =$ _____

6. $5 \times 8 =$ _____

7. $7 \times 5 =$ _____

8. $5 \times 4 =$ _____

9. $5 \times 9 =$ _____

10. $0 \times 5 =$ _____

Teacher Note: Use after Quick Check, page 102, to reteach Unit 4, Lesson 5. **(3)**

Find the product: **6 × 4**.

You can use arrays to help you multiply by **4**.

Think: How many rows?
How many in each row?
How many in all?

$6 × 4 = 24$

Complete. Use an array to help you multiply.

1.

How many rows? _____

How many in each row?

_____

How many in all? _____

$4 × 4 =$ _____

2.

How many rows? _____

How many in each row?

_____

How many in all? _____

$5 ×$ _____ $=$ _____

3.

$3 × 4 =$ _____

4.

$2 × 4 =$ _____

Write the product.

5. $8 × 4 =$ _____

6. $4 × 5 =$ _____

7. $9 × 4 =$ _____

8. $6 × 4 =$ _____

9. $4 × 0 =$ _____

10. $4 × 4 =$ _____

11. $4 × 3 =$ _____

12. $1 × 4 =$ _____

13. $4 × 2 =$ _____

Teacher Note: Use after Quick Check, page 102, to reteach Unit 4, Lesson 6. **(3)**

You can count by tens to help you multiply with **10**.
In the chart, the shaded boxes show counting by tens.

To find **6 × 10**, count the first **6** shaded boxes:
10, 20, 30, 40, 50, 60.

So **6 × 10 = 60**.

1	2	3	4	5	6	7	8	9	10
11	12	13	14	15	16	17	18	19	20
21	22	23	24	25	26	27	28	29	30
31	32	33	34	35	36	37	38	39	40
41	42	43	44	45	46	47	48	49	50
51	52	53	54	55	56	57	58	59	60
61	62	63	64	65	66	67	68	69	70
71	72	73	74	75	76	77	78	79	80
81	82	83	84	85	86	87	88	89	90

Find the product.

1. $8 \times 10 =$ _____

Count **8** shaded boxes:

10, 20, 30, 40, 50,

_____, _____, _____

2. $5 \times 10 =$ _____

Count **5** shaded boxes:

10, 20, _____, _____, _____

3. $3 \times 10 =$ _____

Count **3** shaded boxes:

_____, _____, _____

4. $4 \times 10 =$ _____

Count **4** shaded boxes:

_____, _____, _____, _____

5. $7 \times 10 =$ _____

Count **7** shaded boxes.

6. $9 \times 10 =$ _____

Count **9** shaded boxes.

7. $10 \times 3 =$ _____

8. $10 \times 4 =$ _____

9. $10 \times 9 =$ _____

10. $10 \times 5 =$ _____

11. $0 \times 10 =$ _____

12. $2 \times 10 =$ _____

13. $10 \times 1 =$ _____

14. $6 \times 10 =$ _____

15. $10 \times 8 =$ _____

Teacher Note: Use after Quick Check, page 108, to reteach Unit 4, Lesson 9. **(3)**

Name _____

You can use repeated subtraction to find how many groups of **2** are in this array.

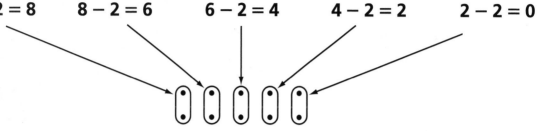

There are **10** dots in the array. Start with **10**.
Keep subtracting **2** until you reach **0**.

$$10 - 2 = 8 \qquad 8 - 2 = 6 \qquad 6 - 2 = 4 \qquad 4 - 2 = 2 \qquad 2 - 2 = 0$$

You subtracted **5** times.

There are **5** groups of **2** in the array.

Use repeated subtraction to show how many groups of 3 can be made from each array.

1.

Total number in array: 12

$12 - 3 = 9$ $\qquad\qquad$ $9 - $ _____ $= $ _____

_____ $- $ _____ $= $ _____ $\qquad$ _____ $- $ _____ $= $ _____

Number of groups: _____

2.

Total number in array: _____

Number of groups: _____

3.

Total number in array: _____

Number of groups: _____

4.

Total number in array: _____

Number of groups: _____

5.

Total number in array: _____

Number of groups: _____

88

Teacher Note: Use before Unit 5, Lesson 1. **(3)**

You can make groups of **2** to complete this division sentence:

$12 \div 2 = ?$

• • • • • •
• • • • • •

Circle as many groups of two as possible. The answer in division is the **quotient:**

$12 \div 2 = 6$

There are **6** groups.

Make groups of 2. Complete the division sentence.

1.

Number of groups: **5**

$10 \div 2 = $ _____

2.

Number of groups: **2**

$4 \div 2 = $ _____

3.

Number of groups: _____

$6 \div 2 = $ _____

4.

Number of groups: _____

$14 \div 2 = $ _____

5. • • • • • •
• • • • • •

Number of groups: _____

$16 \div 2 = $ _____

6. • • • •
• • • •

Number of groups: _____

$8 \div 2 = $ _____

7. •
•

Number of groups: _____

$2 \div 2 = $ _____

8. • • • • • • •
• • • • • • •

Number of groups: _____

$18 \div 2 = $ _____

Teacher Note: Use after Quick Check page 120 to reteach Unit 5, Lesson 1. **(3)**

Operations that undo each other are **inverse** operations.

Addition Sentence	Subtraction Sentence
$2 + 2 + 2 + 2 = 8$	$8 - 2 - 2 - 2 - 2 = 0$

Addition and subtraction are inverse operations.

Multiplication Sentence	Division Sentence
$4 \times 2 = 8$	$8 \div 2 = 4$

You know that $8 \div 2 = 4$ because $4 \times 2 = 8$.

Multiplication and division are inverse operations.

Complete the number sentences.

1.

$6 \div 2 = 3$

because $3 \times 2 =$ _____

2.

$10 \div 2 = 5$

because $5 \times 2 =$ _____

3.

$12 \div 2 = 6$

because _____ $\times 2 =$ _____

4.

$2 \div 2 =$ _____

because _____ $\times 2 =$ _____

5.

$12 \div 2 =$ _____

because _____ $\times$ _____ $=$ _____

6.

$14 \div 2 =$ _____

because _____ $\times 2 =$ _____

7.

$18 \div 2 =$ _____

because _____ $\times$ _____ $=$ _____

8.

$4 \div 2 =$ _____

because _____ $\times 2 =$ _____

Teacher Note: Use after Quick Check page 120 to reteach Unit 5, Lesson 2. (3)

Here are some related facts. These four facts make a **fact family**.

$5 \times 2 = 10$

So $10 \div 2 = 5$

$2 \times 5 = 10$

So $10 \div 5 = 2$

Complete to make a fact family.

1.

$14 \div 2 = 7$

$7 \times 2 = $ _____

$14 \div 7 = $ _____

$2 \times 7 = $ _____

2.

$8 \div 2 = $ _____

$4 \times 2 = $ _____

$8 \div 4 = $ _____

$2 \times 4 = $ _____

---

3. $12 \div 2 = 6$

$12 \div 6 = $ _____

$6 \times 2 = $ _____

$2 \times 6 = $ _____

4. $16 \div 2 = $ _____

$16 \div 8 = $ _____

$8 \times 2 = $ _____

$2 \times 8 = $ _____

5. $2 \div 2 = $ _____

$2 \div 1 = $ _____

$1 \times 2 = $ _____

$2 \times 1 = $ _____

---

6. $6 \div 2 = $ _____

$6 \div 3 = $ _____

_____ $\times 2 = $ _____

_____ $\times$ _____ $= $ _____

7. $18 \div 2 = $ _____

$18 \div 9 = $ _____

_____ $\times 2 = $ _____

_____ $\times$ _____ $= $ _____

Teacher Note: Use after Quick Check page 120 to reteach Unit 5, Lesson 3. **(3)**

⊙ ⊙ ⊙ ⊙

This picture shows:
4 ÷ 1 = 4

There are **4** dots in all.

1 dot is in each group.

There are **4** groups.

This picture shows:
4 ÷ 4 = 1

There are **4** dots in all.

4 dots are in a group.

There is **1** group.

This picture shows:
0 ÷ 4 = 0

There are **0** dots in all.

4 dots are in a group.

There are **0** groups.

Find the quotient.

1. (• • • • • •)

6 ÷ 6 = _____

2.

0 ÷ 3 = _____

3. ⊙ ⊙ ⊙ ⊙ ⊙

5 ÷ 1 = _____

4. (• •)

2 ÷ 2 = _____

Draw a picture to show the division sentence. Write the quotient.

5. 8 ÷ 1 = _____

6. 0 ÷ 9 = _____

7. 6 ÷ 1 = _____

8. 3 ÷ 3 = _____

9. 0 ÷ 7 = _____

10. 9 ÷ 1 = _____

11. 5 ÷ 5 = _____

12. 8 ÷ 8 = _____

Teacher Note: Use after Quick Check page 126 to reteach Unit 5, Lesson 4. **(3)**

Divide: **30 ÷ 5.**

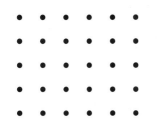

Draw **30** dots.

Put **5** dots in each row or in each column.

Loop each row or column to divide the dots into groups of **5**.

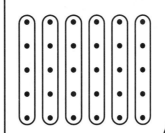

Count the groups.

There are **6** groups of **5** dots.

So **30 ÷ 5 = 6.**

Loop groups of 5. Complete the number sentence.

1.

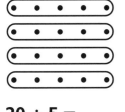

20 ÷ 5 = _____

2.

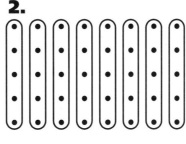

40 ÷ 5 = _____

3.

15 ÷ 5 = _____

Draw a picture to show the division sentence. Then find the quotient.

4. 5 ÷ 5 = _____

5. 35 ÷ 5 = _____

Find the quotient.

6. 40 ÷ 5 = _____

7. 45 ÷ 5 = _____

8. 5 ÷ 5 = _____

9. 20 ÷ 5 = _____

10. 10 ÷ 5 = _____

11. 15 ÷ 5 = _____

12. 30 ÷ 5 = _____

13. 25 ÷ 5 = _____

14. 35 ÷ 5 = _____

Teacher Note: Use after Quick Check page 126 to reteach Unit 5, Lesson 5. **(3)**

These pairs of related facts make a fact family.

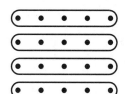

$4 \times 5 = 20$

So $20 \div 5 = 4$

$5 \times 4 = 20$

So $20 \div 4 = 5$

Complete the fact family.

1.

$7 \times 5 =$ _____

$35 \div 5 =$ _____

ART FILE: 700?

$5 \times 7 =$ _____

$35 \div 7 =$ _____

2.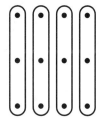

$2 \times 5 =$ _____

$10 \div 5 =$ _____

_____ $\times$ _____ = _____

_____ $\div$ _____ = _____

---

3. $9 \times 5 =$ _____

_____ $\times$ _____ = _____

$45 \div 5 =$ _____

_____ $\div$ _____ = _____

4. $5 \times 6 =$ _____

_____ $\times$ _____ = _____

_____ $\div$ _____ = _____

_____ $\div$ _____ = _____

5. $1 \times 5 =$ _____

_____ $\times$ _____ = _____

_____ $\div$ _____ = _____

_____ $\div$ _____ = _____

6. $5 \times 3 =$ _____

_____ $\times$ _____ = _____

_____ $\div$ _____ = _____

_____ $\div$ _____ = _____

7. $8 \times 5 =$ _____

_____ $\times$ _____ = _____

_____ $\div$ _____ = _____

_____ $\div$ _____ = _____

8. $5 \times 5 =$ _____

_____ $\div$ _____ = _____

_____ $\div$ _____ = _____

Teacher Note: Use after Quick Check page 126 to reteach Unit 5, Lesson 6. **(3)**

These pairs of related facts make a fact family.

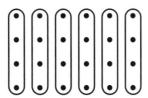

6 × 4 = 24

So 24 ÷ 4 = 6

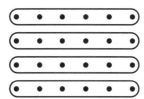

4 × 6 = 24

So 24 ÷ 6 = 4

Complete the fact family.

1.

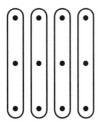

4 × 3 = _____

12 ÷ 3 = _____

3 × 4 = _____

12 ÷ 4 = _____

2.

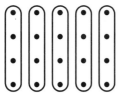

5 × 4 = _____

20 ÷ 4 = _____

_____ × _____ = _____

_____ ÷ _____ = _____

3. 9 × 4 = _____

_____ × _____ = _____

36 ÷ 4 = _____

_____ ÷ _____ = _____

4. 4 × 7 = _____

_____ × _____ = _____

_____ ÷ _____ = _____

_____ ÷ _____ = _____

5. 1 × 4 = _____

_____ × _____ = _____

_____ ÷ _____ = _____

_____ ÷ _____ = _____

6. 4 × 2 = _____

_____ × _____ = _____

_____ ÷ _____ = _____

_____ ÷ _____ = _____

7. 8 × 4 = _____

_____ × _____ = _____

_____ ÷ _____ = _____

_____ ÷ _____ = _____

8. 4 × 4 = _____

_____ ÷ _____ = _____

Teacher Note: Use after Quick Check page 136 to reteach Unit 5, Lesson 8. **(3)**

These pairs of related facts make a fact family.

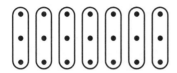

$7 \times 3 = 21$

So $21 \div 3 = 7$

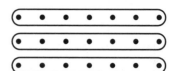

$3 \times 7 = 21$

So $21 \div 7 = 3$

Complete the fact family.

1.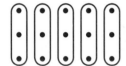

$5 \times 3 =$ _____

$15 \div 3 =$ _____

$3 \times 5 =$ _____

_____ $\div$ _____ $=$ _____

2.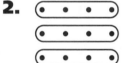

$3 \times 4 =$ _____

$12 \div 4 =$ _____

_____ $\times$ _____ $=$ _____

_____ $\div$ _____ $=$ _____

---

3. $6 \times 3 =$ _____

_____ $\times$ _____ $=$ _____

$18 \div 3 =$ _____

_____ $\div$ _____ $=$ _____

4. $3 \times 2 =$ _____

_____ $\times$ _____ $=$ _____

_____ $\div$ _____ $=$ _____

_____ $\div$ _____ $=$ _____

5. $3 \times 1 =$ _____

_____ $\times$ _____ $=$ _____

_____ $\div$ _____ $=$ _____

_____ $\div$ _____ $=$ _____

6. $9 \times 3 =$ _____

_____ $\times$ _____ $=$ _____

_____ $\div$ _____ $=$ _____

_____ $\div$ _____ $=$ _____

7. $3 \times 8 =$ _____

_____ $\times$ _____ $=$ _____

_____ $\div$ _____ $=$ _____

_____ $\div$ _____ $=$ _____

8. $3 \times 3 =$ _____

_____ $\div$ _____ $=$ _____

Teacher Note: Use after Quick Check page 136 to reteach Unit 5, Lesson 9. **(3)**

The **unit cost** is the cost for one colored pencil. Divide to find the unit cost.

45 ÷ 5 = ?

Colored Pencil Sale
5 for 45¢

Remember: A related multiplication fact can help you with the division. __?__ × 5 = 45

Since **45 ÷ 5 = 9**, then **45¢ ÷ 5 = 9¢**.

One colored pencil costs **9¢**.

Complete the chart to find the unit costs for other items.

	Item	Price	Division Sentence	Unit Cost
1.	pencils	**3 for 15¢**	**15 ÷ 3 = 5**	_____ ¢
2.	pens	**4 for 24¢**	**24 ÷ 4 = 6**	_____ ¢
3.	markers	**4 for 20¢**	**20 ÷ 4 = _____**	_____ ¢
4.	crayons	**6 for 24¢**	**24 ÷ 6 = _____**	_____ ¢
5.	lined paper	**8 sheets for 24¢**		_____ ¢
6.	colored paper	**4 sheets for 8¢**		_____ ¢
7.	erasers	**3 for 18¢**		_____ ¢
8.	stickers	**8 for 32¢**		_____ ¢
9.	pastels	**5 for 40¢**		_____ ¢
10.	folders	**2 for 18¢**		_____ ¢
11.	tape	**4 for 32¢**		_____ ¢
12.	glue sticks	**3 for 21¢**		_____ ¢

Reteach Worksheets

Plane Figures

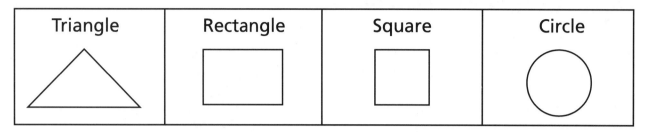

Triangle	Rectangle	Square	Circle

Solid Figures

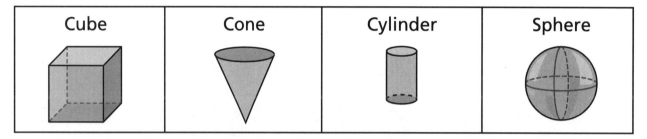

Cube	Cone	Cylinder	Sphere

Use the diagrams of the plane figures. Complete the chart.

	Name of Figure	Number of Sides	Number of Corners
1.	circle	0	_____
2.	triangle	_____	3
3.	rectangle	_____	_____
4.	square	_____	_____

Write the name of the solid figure that matches the picture.

5.   **6.**   **7.**  **8.**

_____ _____ _____ _____

Teacher Note: Use before Unit 6, Lesson 1. **(3)**

This spinner will **always** stop on gray.

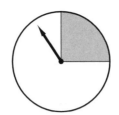

This spinner will **sometimes** stop on gray.

This spinner will **never** stop on gray.

How often will the spinner stop on stripes?
Circle *sometimes*, *always*, or *never*.

1.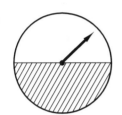

sometimes

always

never

2.

sometimes

always

never

3.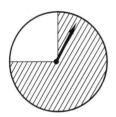

sometimes

always

never

4.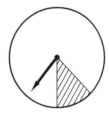

sometimes

always

never

How often will the spinner stop on white?
Circle *sometimes*, *always*, or *never*.

5.

sometimes

always

never

6.

sometimes

always

never

7.

sometimes

always

never

8.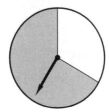

sometimes

always

never

Teacher Note: Use before Unit 6, Lesson 1. **(3)**

Polygon	Name of Polygon	Number of Sides	Number of Corners
△	triangle	3	3
□	square	4	4
▭	rectangle	4	4
⬠	pentagon	5	5
⬡	hexagon	6	6
⯃	octagon	8	8

Complete each sentence. Use the table above.

1. A triangle has _____ sides and _____ corners.

2. A pentagon has _____ sides and _____ corners.

3. A hexagon has _____ sides and _____ corners.

4. A octagon has _____ sides and _____ corners.

Circle the name of the shape.

5.   triangle
rectangle
pentagon

6.   pentagon
hexagon
octagon

7.   triangle
square
octagon

8.   pentagon
hexagon
octagon

9.   rectangle
pentagon
hexagon

10.   square
pentagon
hexagon

Teacher Note: Use after Quick Check page 148 to reteach Unit 6, Lesson 1. **(3)**

You can use the corner of a sheet of paper to tell if an angle is a right angle.

 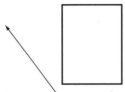

| This is a **right angle**. | This angle is **greater than** a right angle. | This angle is **less than** a right angle. |

The hands of a clock form an angle.

Write if the angle formed is *greater than* a right angle, *less than* a right angle, or is a *right angle*.

Use the corner of a sheet of paper to help you.

1.

_____

_____

2.

_____

_____

3.

_____

_____

4.

_____

_____

5.

_____

_____

6.

_____

_____

Teacher Note: Use after Quick Check page 148 to reteach Unit 6, Lesson 2. **(3)**

Parallel lines are always the same distance apart. They will never meet.

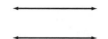

Use a ruler and extend the lines to check if the lines are parallel.

A **quadrilateral** is a polygon with **4** sides. Use a ruler and extend the sides to check if the sides of this quadrilateral are parallel.

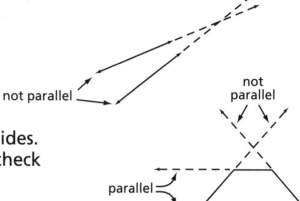

Quadrilaterals		
2 pairs of parallel sides	**1 pair of parallel sides**	**no parallel sides**

Are the lines parallel? Write *yes* or *no*.

1.

2.

3.

4.

_____ _____ _____ _____

How many pairs of parallel sides are there? Write *0, 1,* or *2*.

5.

6.

7.

8.

_____ _____ _____ _____

Teacher Note: Use after Quick Check page 148 to reteach Unit 6, Lesson 3. **(3)**

Equilateral Triangle	**Isosceles Triangle**	**Scalene Triangle**
All sides are the same length.	Two sides are the same length.	All sides are different lengths.

A **right triangle** has one right angle.

Draw a line from the triangle to its name.

1.

scalene triangle

2.

isosceles triangle

3.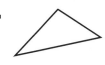

equilateral triangle

Name the triangle. Write *equilateral, isosceles,* or *scalene.*

4.

_____

5.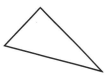

_____

6.

_____

7.

_____

8.

_____

9.

_____

10.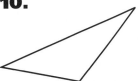

_____

11.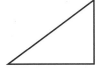

_____

12. Circle all the right triangles on this page.

How many did you find? _____

Teacher Note: Use after Quick Check page 156 to reteach Unit 6, Lesson 4. **(3)**

These two figures are the same size and the same shape. They are **congruent.**

These figures are **not** congruent.

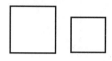

line of symmetry	no symmetry
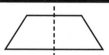	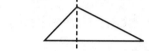
If you fold along the dashed line, the two parts will match exactly.	If you fold along the dashed line, the two parts will **not** match exactly.

Circle the congruent figures.

1.

2.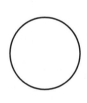

3.

4.

Is the dashed line a line of symmetry? Write *yes* or *no*.

5.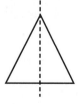

_____

6.

_____

7.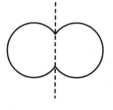

_____

Teacher Note: Use after Quick Check page 156 to reteach Unit 6, Lesson 5. **(3)**

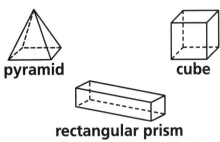

pyramid

cube

rectangular prism

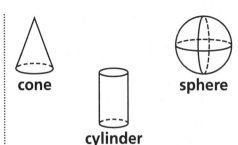

cone

cylinder

sphere

These figures have flat faces, edges, and corners. They do not roll.

These figures have curved surfaces. They can roll.

Circle the name of the solid figure suggested by the picture. Use the figures above to help you.

1.

cone

sphere

cube

2.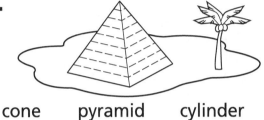

cone   pyramid   cylinder

3.

cube

cylinder

sphere

4.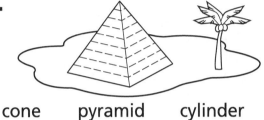

pyramid

rectangular prism

cone

5.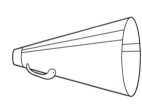

pyramid

sphere

cube

6.

cylinder

rectangular prism

cube

7.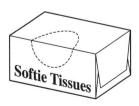

rectangular prism

cone

sphere

8.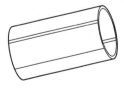

cylinder

rectangular prism

sphere

Teacher Note: Use after Quick Check page 156 to reteach Unit 6, Lesson 7. **(3)**

An **ordered pair** locates a point on a grid.

For the first number in the ordered pair **move across**. ⟶

For the second number in the ordered pair **move up**. ↑

What letter is located at (**2, 5**) on the grid?

Start at **0**.

Move across **2**.

Then move up **5**.

The letter **D** is located at (**2, 5**) on the grid.

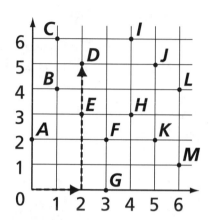

Use the above grid. Write the ordered pair for each letter.

1. A (0, ___)   **2.** H (___ , 3)   **3.** J _____   **4.** M _____

Use the above grid. Write the letter located by the ordered pair.

5. (1, 6) ____   **6.** (3, 2) ____   **7.** (1, 4) ____   **8.** (5, 2) ____

9. (6, 4) ____   **10.** (2, 3) ____   **11.** (4, 6) ____   **12.** (3, 0) ____

Use the grid below. Write the ordered pairs that are used to make the figure.

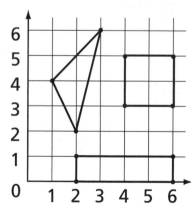

13. triangle

_____

14. square

_____

15. rectangle

_____

Teacher Note: Use after Quick Check page 162 to reteach Unit 6, Lesson 9. **(3)**

The **tally chart** shows the favorite
colors of Mrs. Kelley's third grade
students.

The ||||| mark means **5** tally marks.

Six students chose red as their
favorite color.

Mrs. Kelley's Class		
Color	Tally	Number
Red	|||| |	6
Blue	|||| ||||	10
Green	|||| |||	8
Yellow	||||	4
Pink	||||	5
Orange	|||	3

Use the tally chart above to complete exercises 1–10.
**Draw a line to match how many students chose the
color as their favorite.**

1. Yellow   **10**

2. Blue   **8**

3. Green   **4**

Solve.

4. How many students chose pink as their favorite color? _____

5. How many more students chose pink as their favorite color
than yellow? _____

6. How many more students chose green as their favorite color
than yellow? _____

7. How many more students chose green as their favorite color
than red? _____

8. What is the most popular color in the class? _____

9. What is the least popular color in the class? _____

10. How many people participated in the survey? _____

Teacher Note: Use after Quick Check page 162 to reteach Unit 6, Lesson 10. **(3)**

What is the chance the spinner will stop on gray?

 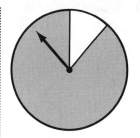 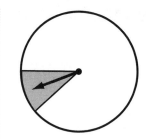 

certain	**likely**	**unlikely**	**impossible**
The spinner is all gray.	Most of the spinner is gray.	Most of the spinner is white.	The spinner is all white.

What is the chance the spinner will stop on white?
Circle *certain, likely, unlikely,* or *impossible.*

1.

certain

likely

unlikely

impossible

2.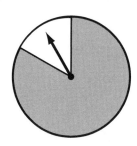

certain

likely

unlikely

impossible

3.

certain

likely

unlikely

impossible

4.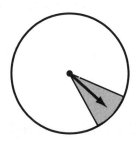

certain

likely

unlikely

impossible

What are the chances the statement will happen?
Write *certain, likely, unlikely,* or *impossible.*

5. Mail will be delivered to your home this month.

_____

6. This month will have more than **27** days.

_____

7. It will snow in San Diego on May 15 and June 15.

_____

8. You will toss a penny up in the air and it will not come down.

_____

Teacher Note: Use after Quick Check page 166 to reteach Unit 6, Lesson 11. **(3)**

Mr. Capizio's class recorded the daily high temperature for the first part of May. The **line plot** shows the results.

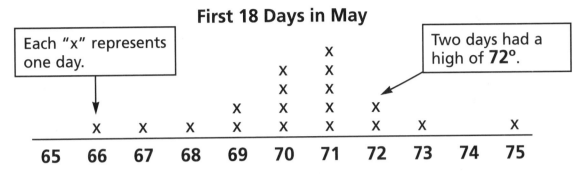

First 18 Days in May

Each "x" represents one day.

Two days had a high of **72°**.

| 65 | 66 | 67 | 68 | 69 | 70 | 71 | 72 | 73 | 74 | 75 |

Temperature in degrees F°

Most of the high temperatures recorded were about **70°** or **71°**. You might predict the next day's temperature to be about **71°**.

Write the number of days the temperature was recorded.

1. 65° _____ **2.** 67° _____ **3.** 70° _____ **4.** 71° _____ **5.** 72° _____

Use the line plot above to answer the questions.

6. Which temperature occurred most often? _____

7. Which temperatures were not the high temperature for any of the first **18** days in May? _____

8. For how many days was the temperature recorded? _____

9. Is it possible that the temperature tomorrow will be about **75°**? Explain. _____

10. Is it likely the temperature tomorrow will be above **90°**? Explain. _____

11. Is it likely that the temperature tomorrow will be above **60°**? Explain. _____

Teacher Note: Use after Quick Check page 166 to reteach Unit 6, Lesson 12. **(3)**

These figures are divided into equal parts.

These figures are *not* divided into equal parts.

You can write a fraction to tell how much is shaded.

The top number, or **numerator,**
tells how many parts are shaded. $\longrightarrow$ $\dfrac{5}{6}$

The bottom number, or **denominator,** $\longrightarrow$
tells how many equal parts there are.

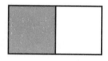

$\frac{1}{2}$ of the rectangle
is shaded.

$\frac{3}{4}$ of the stars are
shaded.

$\frac{2}{3}$ of the circle
is shaded.

Is the figure divided into equal parts? Write *yes* or *no*.

1.   **2.**   **3.**   **4.**

_____ _____ _____ _____

Write a fraction that tells how much is shaded.

5.  **6.** 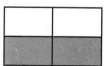 **7.**   **8.**

_____ _____ _____ _____

Teacher Note: Use before Unit 7, Lesson 1. (3)

Each model is divided into **6** equal parts.
Each part is $\frac{1}{6}$ of the whole.

largest ⟶ 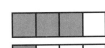 $\frac{4}{6}$ of the whole is shaded.

$\frac{3}{6}$ of the whole is shaded.

smallest ⟶ $\frac{2}{6}$ of the whole is shaded.

$\frac{4}{6}$ is greater than $\frac{3}{6}$, and $\frac{3}{6}$ is greater than $\frac{2}{6}$.

$$\frac{4}{6} > \frac{3}{6} \text{ and } \frac{3}{6} > \frac{2}{6}$$

In order from greatest to least, the fractions are $\frac{4}{6}, \frac{3}{6}, \frac{2}{6}$.

Compare. Write >, <, or =.

1.

$\frac{1}{3} \bigcirc \frac{2}{3}$

2.

$\frac{3}{4} \bigcirc \frac{1}{4}$

3.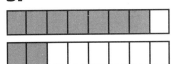

$\frac{7}{8} \bigcirc \frac{2}{8}$

4.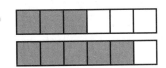

$\frac{3}{6} \bigcirc \frac{5}{6}$

5.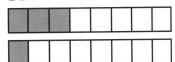

$\frac{3}{8} \bigcirc \frac{1}{8}$

6.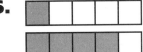

$\frac{1}{5} \bigcirc \frac{4}{5}$

Write the fractions in order from greatest to least.

7.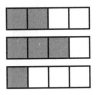

_____

8.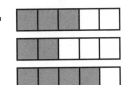

_____

9.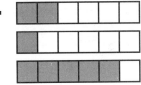

_____

Teacher Note: Use After Quick Check page 178 to reteach Unit 7, Lesson 2. **(3)**

$\frac{2}{3}$ and $\frac{4}{6}$ are **equivalent fractions.**

They show the same amount.

$$\frac{2}{3} = \frac{4}{6}$$

| $\frac{1}{3}$ | $\frac{1}{3}$ | $\frac{1}{3}$ | $\frac{2}{3}$ |

| $\frac{1}{6}$ | $\frac{1}{6}$ | $\frac{1}{6}$ | $\frac{1}{6}$ | $\frac{1}{6}$ | $\frac{1}{6}$ | $\frac{4}{6}$ |

Write the equivalent fraction.

1.

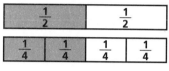

$$\frac{1}{2} = \frac{}{4}$$

2.

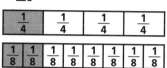

$$\frac{1}{4} = \frac{}{8}$$

3.

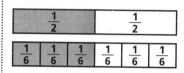

$$\frac{1}{2} = \frac{}{6}$$

4.

$$\frac{3}{4} = \frac{6}{}$$

5.

$$\frac{1}{3} = \frac{2}{}$$

6.

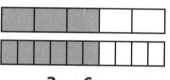

$$\frac{3}{5} = \frac{6}{}$$

Shade the second bar to show the equivalent fraction.
Complete the fraction.

7.

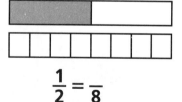

$$\frac{1}{2} = \frac{}{8}$$

8.

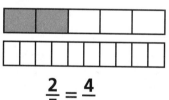

$$\frac{2}{5} = \frac{4}{}$$

9.

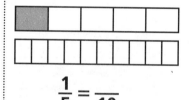

$$\frac{1}{5} = \frac{}{10}$$

10.

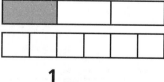

$$\frac{1}{3} = \frac{}{6}$$

11.

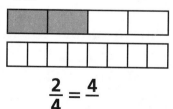

$$\frac{2}{4} = \frac{4}{}$$

12.

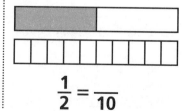

$$\frac{1}{2} = \frac{}{10}$$

Teacher Note: Use After Quick Check page 178 to reteach Unit 7, Lesson 3. **(3)**

Here are **12** stars.

The stars are divided into **4** equal groups.

To find $\frac{1}{4}$ of the stars shade 1 of the 4 groups.

$\frac{1}{4}$ of the stars are shaded.

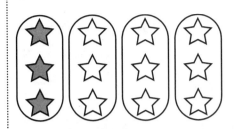

$\frac{1}{4}$ of **12** stars = **3** stars

Shade then write the number. Remember: the denominator of the fraction tells how many equal groups to make.

1.

$\frac{1}{2}$ of **6** = _____

2.

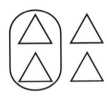

$\frac{1}{2}$ of **4** = _____

3.

$\frac{1}{2}$ of **10** = _____

4.

$\frac{1}{3}$ of **6** = _____

5.

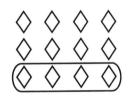

$\frac{1}{3}$ of **12** = _____

6.

$\frac{1}{4}$ of **8** = _____

7.

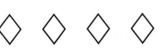

$\frac{1}{2}$ of **8** = _____

8.

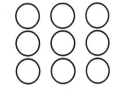

$\frac{1}{3}$ of **9** = _____

9.

$\frac{1}{2}$ of **16** = _____

Reteach Worksheets

Teacher Note: Use before Unit 7, Lesson 1. **(3)**

You can use division to find a fraction of a
number if the numerator of the fraction is **1**.

Find $\frac{1}{3}$ of **9**. Think: **9 ÷ 3 = ?**

Find $\frac{1}{4}$ of **8**. Think: **8 ÷ 4 = ?**

There are **9** triangles.

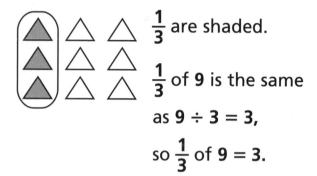 $\frac{1}{3}$ are shaded.

$\frac{1}{3}$ of **9** is the same

as **9 ÷ 3 = 3**,

so $\frac{1}{3}$ of **9 = 3**.

There are **8** circles.

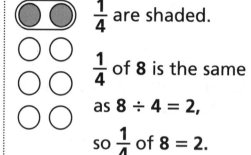 $\frac{1}{4}$ are shaded.

$\frac{1}{4}$ of **8** is the same

as **8 ÷ 4 = 2**,

so $\frac{1}{4}$ of **8 = 2**.

Draw loops to show the fraction. Then complete.

1. ☆ ☆ ☆ ☆ ☆
☆ ☆ ☆ ☆ ☆

Think: **10 ÷ 5 =** _____

$\frac{1}{5}$ of **10 =** _____

2. △ △ △
△ △ △

Think: **6 ÷ 3 = 2**

$\frac{1}{3}$ of **6 =** _____

3. ◇ ◇ ◇ ◇
◇ ◇ ◇ ◇
◇ ◇ ◇ ◇

Think: **12 ÷ 4 =** _____

$\frac{1}{4}$ of **12 =** _____

Complete.

4. $\frac{1}{2}$ of **12 =** _____

Think: **12 ÷ 2 =** __6__

5. $\frac{1}{4}$ of **16 =** _____

Think: **16 ÷ 4 =** _____

6. $\frac{1}{3}$ of **12 =** _____

Think: **12 ÷ 3 =** _____

7. $\frac{1}{2}$ of **16 =** _____

Think: **16 ÷ 2 =** _____

8. $\frac{1}{3}$ of **15 =** _____

Think: **15 ÷ 3 =** _____

9. $\frac{1}{5}$ of **5 =** _____

Think: **5 ÷ 5 =** _____

Teacher Note: Use After Quick Check page 182 to reteach Unit 7, Lesson 5. **(3)**

Fractions and whole numbers can be used
to name numbers greater than **1**.

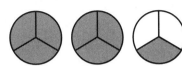

2 wholes are shaded and $\frac{1}{3}$ of another whole is shaded.

The mixed number for the shaded parts is $2\frac{1}{3}$.

Read the mixed number as "two and one third."

Write a mixed number for the shaded parts.

1.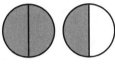

$1\frac{\square}{2}$

2.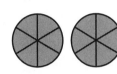

$2\frac{\square}{6}$

3. 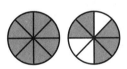 _____

4. 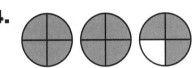 _____

5. 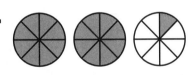 _____

6. 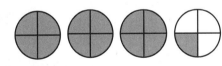 _____

7. 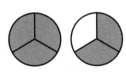 _____

8. 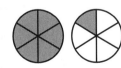 _____

Write the mixed number.

9. one and one fourth _____

10. one and five eighths _____

11. two and one sixth _____

12. one and two thirds _____

13. two and three fourths _____

14. three and one half _____

Teacher Note: Use After Quick Check page 188 to reteach Unit 7, Lesson 8. **(3)**

2 × 4 = ?　　　　　2 × 4 = 8

3 × 5 = ?　　　　　3 × 5 = 15

Find each product.

1. 0 × 0 = __0__

1 × 0 = __0__

2 × 0 = _____

3 × 0 = _____

4 × 0 = _____

5 × 0 = _____

6 × 0 = _____

7 × 0 = _____

8 × 0 = _____

9 × 0 = _____

2. 0 × 1 = _____

1 × 1 = _____

2 × 1 = _____

3 × 1 = _____

4 × 1 = _____

5 × 1 = _____

6 × 1 = _____

7 × 1 = _____

8 × 1 = _____

9 × 1 = _____

3. 0 × 2 = _____

1 × 2 = _____

2 × 2 = _____

3 × 2 = _____

4 × 2 = _____

5 × 2 = _____

6 × 2 = _____

7 × 2 = _____

8 × 2 = _____

9 × 2 = _____

4. 0 × 3 = _____

1 × 3 = _____

2 × 3 = _____

3 × 3 = _____

4 × 3 = _____

5 × 3 = _____

6 × 3 = _____

7 × 3 = _____

8 × 3 = _____

9 × 3 = _____

5. 0 × 4 = _____

1 × 4 = _____

2 × 4 = _____

3 × 4 = _____

4 × 4 = _____

5 × 4 = _____

6 × 4 = _____

7 × 4 = _____

8 × 4 = _____

9 × 4 = _____

6. 0 × 5 = _____

1 × 5 = _____

2 × 5 = _____

3 × 5 = _____

4 × 5 = _____

5 × 5 = _____

6 × 5 = _____

7 × 5 = _____

8 × 5 = _____

9 × 5 = _____

Teacher Note: Use before Unit 8, Lesson 1. **(3)**

Write the related facts.

$4 \times 5 = 20$ So, $20 \div 5 = 4$

$5 \times 4 = 20$ So, $20 \div 4 = 5$

Write the related facts.

1. $8 \times 2 = 16$

$2 \times 8 =$ _____

$16 \div 2 = 8$

$16 \div 8 =$ _____

2. $3 \times 5 =$ _____

_____ $\times$ _____ = _____

$15 \div 5 =$ _____

_____ $\div$ _____ = _____

3. $9 \times 4 =$ _____

_____ $\times$ _____ = _____

$36 \div 4 =$ _____

_____ $\div$ _____ = _____

4. $7 \times 3 =$ _____

_____ $\times$ _____ = _____

_____ $\div$ _____ = _____

_____ $\div$ _____ = _____

5. $8 \times 5 =$ _____

_____ $\times$ _____ = _____

_____ $\div$ _____ = _____

_____ $\div$ _____ = _____

6. $3 \times 2 =$ _____

_____ $\times$ _____ = _____

_____ $\div$ _____ = _____

_____ $\div$ _____ = _____

7. $1 \times 5 =$ _____

_____ $\times$ _____ = _____

_____ $\div$ _____ = _____

_____ $\div$ _____ = _____

8. $7 \times 4 =$ _____

_____ $\times$ _____ = _____

_____ $\div$ _____ = _____

_____ $\div$ _____ = _____

9. $8 \times 3 =$ _____

_____ $\times$ _____ = _____

_____ $\div$ _____ = _____

_____ $\div$ _____ = _____

10. $7 \times 5 =$ _____

_____ $\times$ _____ = _____

_____ $\div$ _____ = _____

_____ $\div$ _____ = _____

11. $6 \times 4 =$ _____

_____ $\times$ _____ = _____

_____ $\div$ _____ = _____

_____ $\div$ _____ = _____

12. $9 \times 2 =$ _____

_____ $\times$ _____ = _____

_____ $\div$ _____ = _____

_____ $\div$ _____ = _____

Reteach Worksheets

Teacher Note: Usebefore Unit 8, Lesson 1. **(3)**

$8 \times 6 = ?$

Think: **8** groups of **6**

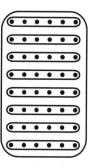

$$8 \times 6 = 6 + 6 + 6 + 6 + 6 + 6 + 6 + 6 = 48$$

$8 \times 6 = 48$, so **48 ÷ 8 = 6** and **48 ÷ 6 = 8**.

Think of groups of 6 to help you multiply. Write the product.

1. $7 \times 6 = $ _____

Think: **7** groups of **6**

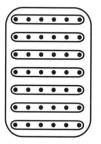

2. $9 \times 6 = $ _____

Think: **9** groups of **6**

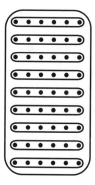

3. $6 \times 6 = $ _____

Think: **6** groups of **6**

4. $4 \times 6 = $ _____

Think: **4** groups of **6**

Find each product.

5. $6 \times 6 = $ _____   **6.** $4 \times 6 = $ _____   **7.** $2 \times 6 = $ _____

8. $8 \times 6 = $ _____   **9.** $3 \times 6 = $ _____   **10.** $1 \times 6 = $ _____

11. $7 \times 6 = $ _____   **12.** $9 \times 6 = $ _____   **13.** $5 \times 6 = $ _____

Find each quotient. Use the products above to help you.

14. $24 \div 6 = $ _____   **15.** $48 \div 6 = $ _____   **16.** $42 \div 6 = $ _____

17. $12 \div 6 = $ _____   **18.** $30 \div 6 = $ _____   **19.** $18 \div 6 = $ _____

20. $36 \div 6 = $ _____   **21.** $6 \div 6 = $ _____   **22.** $54 \div 6 = $ _____

Teacher Note: Use After Quick Check page 204 to reteach Unit 8, Lesson 1. **(3)**

9 × 7 = ?

Think: 9 groups of 7

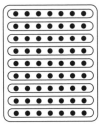

$$9 \times 7 = 7 + 7 + 7 + 7 + 7 + 7 + 7 + 7 + 7 = 63$$

9 × 7 = 63, so **63 ÷ 9 = 7** and **63 ÷ 7 = 9**

Write the product. Think of groups of 7 to help you multiply.

1. 8 × 7 = _____

Think: **8** groups of **7**

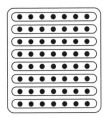

2. 7 × 7 = _____

Think: **7** groups of **7**

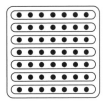

3. 5 × 7 = _____

Think: **5** groups of **7**

4. 6 × 7 = _____

Think: **6** groups of **7**

Find each product.

5. 4 × 7 = _____

6. 3 × 7 = _____

7. 0 × 7 = _____

8. 7 × 7 = _____

9. 8 × 7 = _____

10. 2 × 7 = _____

11. 6 × 7 = _____

12. 9 × 7 = _____

13. 5 × 7 = _____

Find each quotient. Use the products above to help you.

14. 21 ÷ 7 = _____

15. 49 ÷ 7 = _____

16. 42 ÷ 7 = _____

17. 63 ÷ 7 = _____

18. 56 ÷ 7 = _____

19. 35 ÷ 7 = _____

20. 14 ÷ 7 = _____

21. 7 ÷ 7 = _____

22. 28 ÷ 7 = _____

Teacher Note: Use after Quick Check page 204 to reteach Unit 8, Lesson 2. **(3)**

119

Reteach Worksheets

Name _____

$7 \times 8 = ?$

Think: 7 groups of 8

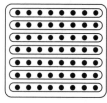

$$7 \times 8 = 8 + 8 + 8 + 8 + 8 + 8 + 8 = 56$$

$7 \times 8 = 56$, so $56 \div 8 = 7$ and $56 \div 7 = 8$.

**Write the product. Think of groups of 8 to
help you multiply.**

1. $9 \times 8 =$ _____

Think: **9** groups of **8**

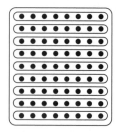

2. $6 \times 8 =$ _____

Think: **6** groups of **8**

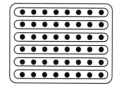

3. $3 \times 8 =$ _____

Think: **3** groups of **8**

4. $8 \times 8 =$ _____

Think: **8** groups of **8**

Find each product.

5. $5 \times 8 =$ _____

6. $4 \times 8 =$ _____

7. $1 \times 8 =$ _____

8. $9 \times 8 =$ _____

9. $3 \times 8 =$ _____

10. $2 \times 8 =$ _____

11. $7 \times 8 =$ _____

12. $6 \times 8 =$ _____

13. $8 \times 8 =$ _____

**Find each quotient. Use the products above
to help you.**

14. $24 \div 8 =$ _____

15. $8 \div 8 =$ _____

16. $40 \div 8 =$ _____

17. $48 \div 8 =$ _____

18. $56 \div 8 =$ _____

19. $32 \div 8 =$ _____

20. $16 \div 8 =$ _____

21. $72 \div 8 =$ _____

22. $64 \div 8 =$ _____

Teacher Note: Use after Quick Check page 204 to reteach Unit 8, Lesson 4. **(3)**

These **14** squares are divided into groups of **4**.

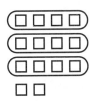

3 R2 ←	**3** groups with **2** left over
4)14 ←	squares in all
− 12 ←	**3 × 4 = 12** squares used
2 ←	**2** squares left over

The quotient and remainder are written **3 R2**.

Use the models. Write the quotient and remainder.

1.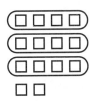

2)11 R1

2.

3)17 R2

3.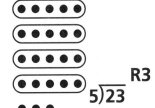

5)23 R3

4.

2)15 R____

5.

5)12 R____

6.

3)14 R____

7.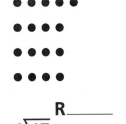

6)14 R____

8.

4)17 R____

9.

7)16 R____

Is this division correct?

$$6\overline{)19} \quad \begin{array}{r} 3\,R1 \\ \end{array}$$
$$\underline{-18}$$
$$1$$

To check division:

| First, multiply the quotient and the divisor. $3 \times 6 = 18$ | Then, add the remainder. $18 + 1 = 19$ | Compare the sum to the dividend. Since $19 = 19$, the division is correct. |

Complete.

1.
$$4\overline{)21} \quad \begin{array}{r} 5\,R1 \\ \end{array}$$
$$\underline{-20}$$
$$1$$

$5 \times 4 +$ _____ $=$ _____ $+$ _____ $= 21$

2.
$$5\overline{)17} \quad \begin{array}{r} 3\,R2 \\ \end{array}$$
$$\underline{-15}$$
$$2$$

$3 \times$ _____ $+$ _____ $=$ _____ $+$ _____ $=$ _____

Find the quotient and remainder. Check by multiplying and adding.

3.
$$3\overline{)14} \quad \underline{}\,R\underline{}$$
$$\underline{-12}$$

_____ $\times 3 +$ _____ $= 14$

4.
$$7\overline{)25} \quad \underline{}\,R\underline{}$$

_____ $\times 7 +$ _____ $= 25$

5.
$$5\overline{)24} \quad \underline{}\,R\underline{}$$

_____ $\times$ _____ $+$ _____ $= 24$

6.
$$6\overline{)32} \quad \underline{}\,R\underline{}$$

_____ $\times$ _____ $+$ _____ $= 32$

Teacher Note: Use after Quick Check page 218 to reteach Unit 8, Lesson 9. **(3)**

When you solve some problems, you have to decide whether to use or drop the remainder.

Sami needs **14** party hats. There are **5** party hats in a package. How many packages does Sami need to buy?

Divide: **14 ÷ 5**

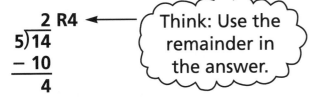

Think: Use the remainder in the answer.

Sami will not have enough hats if she buys **2** packages. Sami needs to buy **3** packages.

Mark's sportscard album holds **4** cards per page. He has **17** cards. How many pages will be completely filled?

Divide: **17 ÷ 4**

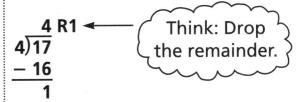

Think: Drop the remainder.

There will be **4** pages completely filled.

Solve.

1. Kayla has **10** apples. She puts **3** apples in each bag. How many apples does she have left?

Divide: **10 ÷ 3**

Think: Use the remainder as the answer.

_____

2. José has **23** marbles to put in boxes. A box holds **5** marbles. How many boxes will he need for all the marbles?

Divide: **23 ÷ 5**

Think: Use the remainder in the answer.

_____

3. A florist has **25** roses to put in vases. Each vase holds **4** roses. How many vases will be completely full?

Think: Drop the remainder.

_____

4. There are **20** children in Ms. Walker's class. She puts the children in groups of **3**. How many groups are there?

Think: Use the remainder in the answer.

_____

Teacher Note: Use after Quick Check page 218 to reteach Unit 8, Lesson 10. **(3)**

Look for the pattern.

8 × 100 = ?
> Think: **8 × 1 = 8**
> **8 × 10 = 80**
> So **8 × 100 = 800**

3 × 200 = ?
> Think: **3 × 2 = 6**
> **3 × 20 = 60**
> So **3 × 200 = 600**

7 × 200 = ?
> Think: **7 × 2 = 14**
> **7 × 20 = 140**
> So **7 × 200 = 1,400**

5 × 600 = ?
> Think: **5 × 6 = 30**
> **5 × 60 = 300**
> So **5 × 600 = 3,000**

There are always at least **2** zeros in the product
when you multiply with multiples of **100**.

Find the products.

1. 3 × 300 = _____   **2.** 4 × 800 = _____   **3.** 2 × 900 = _____

4. 7 × 300 = _____   **5.** 6 × 500 = _____   **6.** 3 × 400 = _____

7. 2 × 400 = _____   **8.** 5 × 700 = _____   **9.** 6 × 400 = _____

10. 6 × 200 = _____   **11.** 7 × 400 = _____   **12.** 5 × 500 = _____

13. 2 × 200 = _____   **14.** 2 × 300 = _____   **15.** 6 × 200 = _____

16. 3 × 900 = _____   **17.** 9 × 300 = _____   **18.** 4 × 500 = _____

19. 2 × 600 = _____   **20.** 4 × 400 = _____   **21.** 6 × 100 = _____

22. 8 × 600 = _____   **23.** 8 × 200 = _____   **24.** 2 × 800 = _____

25. 2 × 500 = _____   **26.** 3 × 600 = _____   **27.** 7 × 400 = _____

28. 8 × 400 = _____   **29.** 6 × 600 = _____   **30.** 3 × 500 = _____

Teacher Note: Use before Unit 9, Lesson 1. **(3)**

Find 43 × 2.

Tens	Ones
4	3
×	2
	6

Tens	Ones
4	3
×	2
8	6

Find the products. Multiply the ones, then the tens.

1.

Tens	Ones
2	3
×	2
	6

2.

Tens	Ones
3	1
×	3
	3

3.

Tens	Ones
4	2
×	2
	4

4.

Tens	Ones
1	4
×	2

5.

Tens	Ones
5	8
×	1

6.

Tens	Ones
1	2
×	4

7.

Tens	Ones
3	4
×	2

8.

Tens	Ones
2	3
×	3

9.

Tens	Ones
1	3
×	3

10.

Tens	Ones
2	2
×	3

11.

Tens	Ones
2	0
×	4

12.

Tens	Ones
3	9
×	1

Find 38 × 2.

Tens	Ones
3	8
×	2

Tens	Ones
1	
3	8
×	2
	6

Tens	Ones
1	
3	8
×	2
7	6

Find the products.

1.

Tens	Ones
1	
4	6
×	2
	2

2.

Tens	Ones
1	
2	5
×	3
	5

3.

Tens	Ones
2	
1	7
×	4
	8

4.

Tens	Ones
2	7
×	3

5.

Tens	Ones
2	3
×	4

6.

Tens	Ones
4	8
×	2

7.

Tens	Ones
2	4
×	4

8.

Tens	Ones
2	9
×	3

9.

Tens	Ones
3	5
×	2

Multiply.

10. 35
  × 4

11. 46
  × 3

12. 27
  × 5

13. 36
  × 3

14. 67
  × 2

Teacher Note: Use after Quick Check page 228 to reteach Unit 9, Lesson 2. **(3)**

Find 231 × 4.

H	T	O
	2	3	1
×			4
			4

H	T	O
	2	3	1
×			4
		2	4

[1]	H	T	O
	2	3	1
×			4
	9	2	4

Find the product.

1.

[2]	H	T	O
	1	3	1
×			7
		1	7

2.

[1]	H	T	O
	3	6	2
×			2
		2	4

3.

[1]	H	T	O
	2	5	3
×			3
		5	9

4.

☐	H	T	O
	3	7	0
×			2
			0

5.

☐	H	T	O
	2	5	3
×			2
			6

6.

☐	H	T	O
	2	4	2
×			4
			8

7.

☐	H	T	O
	3	8	1
×			2

8.

☐	H	T	O
	2	8	2
×			3

9.

☐	H	T	O
	1	5	2
×			4

10.

☐	H	T	O
	2	8	3
×			3

11.

☐	H	T	O
	2	6	1
×			3

12.

☐	H	T	O
	1	9	2
×			4

Teacher Note: Use after Quick Check page 234 to reteach Unit 9, Lesson 5. **(3)**

Find 409 × 5.

TH	H	T	O
	4	0	9
×			5
			5

TH	H	T	O
		[4]	
	4	0	9
×			5
		4	5

TH	H	T	O
		[4]	
	4	0	9
×			5
2	0	4	5

Multiply.

1.
```
    4
  3 0 5
×     8
```

2.
```
    1
  4 6 0
×     3
```

3.
```
    3
  2 0 7
×     5
```

4.
```
    2
  5 0 9
×     3
```

5.
```
    1
  6 0 2
×     5
```

6.
```
   □
  6 9 0
×     3
```

7.
```
   □
  2 0 5
×     5
```

8.
```
   □
  4 0 9
×     6
```

9.
```
   □
  4 2 0
×     5
```

10.
```
   □
  7 0 8
×     5
```

11.
```
   □
  5 0 2
×     6
```

12.
```
   □
  6 5 0
×     3
```

13.
```
   □
  1 0 9
×     8
```

14.
```
   □
  3 0 6
×     5
```

15.
```
   □
  8 0 2
×     6
```

16.
```
   □
  6 0 2
×     7
```

17.
```
   □
  9 0 4
×     4
```

18.
```
   □
  4 8 0
×     5
```

19.
```
   □
  7 9 0
×     2
```

20.
```
   □
  3 0 8
×     5
```

Teacher Note: Use after Quick Check page 240 to reteach Unit 9, Lesson 7. **(3)**

You can use different kinds of objects to measure
things. If you use your hand to measure the width of
this sheet of paper, it will probably measure about
two hand lengths.

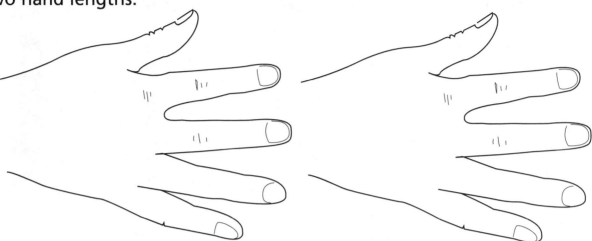

**Estimate the measure of each object using the length of
your hand. Then measure each object using your hand.**

1. The height of your desk

Estimate: _____

Measure: _____

2. The width of your desk

Estimate: _____

Measure: _____

3. The length of the chalkboard

Estimate: _____

Measure: _____

4. Your height

Estimate: _____

Measure: _____

**Estimate the measure of each object using the width
of your thumb. Then measure each object using
your thumb.**

5. The length of a sheet of paper

Estimate: _____

Measure: _____

6. The width of a book

Estimate: _____

Measure: _____

7. The length of a pencil

Estimate: _____

Measure: _____

8. The length of your hand

Estimate: _____

Measure: _____

You can use **inches, feet**, or **yards** to measure some lengths.

| 12 inches = 1 foot |
| 3 feet = 1 yard |

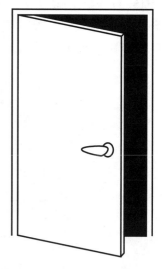

The eraser is about
2 inches long.

The child is about
2 feet tall.

The door is about
2 yards tall.

Loop the better unit for measuring.

1. the length of your thumb

  a. inch   **b.** foot

2. the height of a desk

  a. foot   **b.** yard

3. the height of a door

  a. inch   **b.** yard

4. the length of a pencil

  a. inch   **b.** yard

5. the length of a bicycle

  a. inch   **b.** foot

6. the length of a room

  a. inch   **b.** foot

7. the length of a football field

  a. foot   **b.** yard

8. the width of a door

  a. foot   **b.** yard

9. the length of a paintbrush

  a. inch   **b.** foot

10. the length of a swimming pool

  a. foot   **b.** yard

11. the height of your teacher

  a. inch   **b.** foot

12. the width of a book

  a. inch   **b.** foot

Teacher Note: Use before Unit 10, Lesson 1. **(3)**

You can use centimeters or meters to measure some
lengths.

> **100** centimeters = **1** meter

The paper clip is about
3 centimeters long.

The bicycle is about **1** meter tall.

Loop the better unit for measuring.

1. the length of your thumb

    a. centimeter   **b.** meter

2. the thickness of a magazine

    a. centimeter   **b.** meter

3. the height of a fence

    a. centimeter   **b.** meter

4. the length of a crayon

    a. centimeter   **b.** meter

5. the length of a kitten

    a. centimeter   **b.** meter

6. the length of a hallway

    a. centimeter   **b.** meter

7. the length of a soccer field

    a. centimeter   **b.** meter

8. the width of a notebook

    a. centimeter   **b.** meter

9. the length of a toothbrush

    a. centimeter   **b.** meter

10. the length of a bus

    a. centimeter   **b.** meter

11. the length of a playground

    a. centimeter   **b.** meter

12. the height of a building

    a. centimeter   **b.** meter

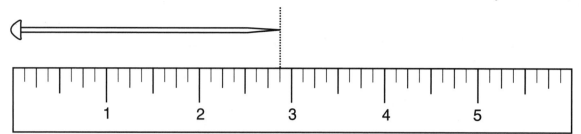

Measure to the **nearest inch**.	Measure to the **nearest half inch**.
Find the inch marks that the object is between. Think: It is between **2** and **3**.	Find the inch mark and the half-inch mark that the object is between.
	Think: It is between $2\frac{1}{2}$ and **3**.
Write the mark it is closer to. It is closer to **3** in.	Write the mark it is closer to. It is closer to **3** in.

Measure to the nearest inch.

1.

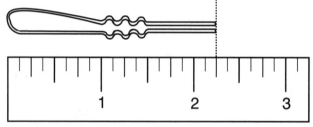

_____

2.

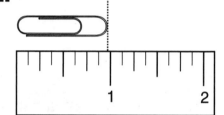

_____

3.

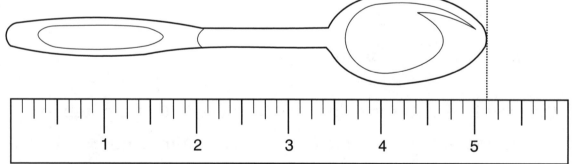

_____

4.

 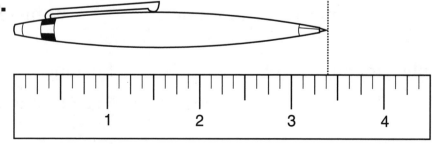

Teacher Note: Use after Quick Check page 256 to reteach Unit 10, Lesson 1. **(3)**

Liquid Measures
2 cups (c) = **1** pint (pt) **2** pints = **1** quart (qt) **4** quarts = **1** gallon (gal)

Weight
16 ounces (oz) = **1** pound (lb)

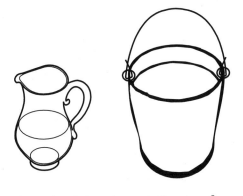

A pitcher holds about **2** qt of water.

A bucket holds about **2** gal of water.

A pear weighs about **5** oz.

A bag of potatoes weighs about **5** lb.

Loop the better estimate.

1. glass of milk

  a. 1 c   **b. 1** qt

2. pot of soup

  a. 2 c   **b. 2** qt

3. a kitchen sink

  a. 2 pt   **b. 2** gal

4. a cereal bowl

  a. 1 c   **b. 1** qt

5. a flower vase

  a. 2 c   **b. 2** gal

6. a car's tank of gas

  a. 15 c   **b. 15** gal

7. a lamp

  a. 4 oz   **b. 4** lb

8. an orange

  a. 8 oz   **b. 8** lb

9. a pencil

  a. 2 oz   **b. 2** lb

10. a light bulb

  a. 3 oz   **b. 3** lb

Teacher Note: Use after Quick Check page 256 to reteach Unit 10, Lesson 2. **(3)**

Each mark on the thermometer is
2°F more than the mark below it.

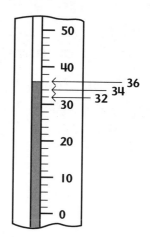

To read the **Fahrenheit** thermometer,
read across from the top of the
liquid to the number on the
thermometer.

The liquid is **3** marks above **30°**.
You can count by 2s from **30**:
30°, 32°, 34°, 36°.

The thermometer shows a temperature of **36°F.**

Use the thermometer to write the temperature.

1.

Think:
20°, 22°, 24°

2.

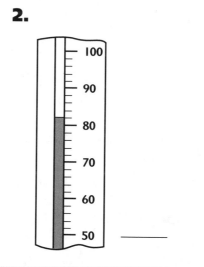

3.

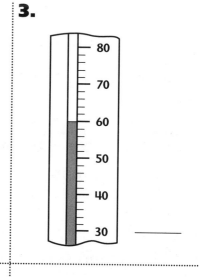

4.

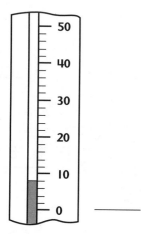

5.

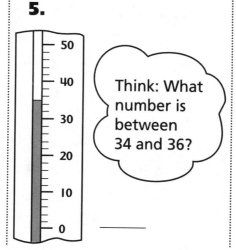

Think: What
number is
between
34 and 36?

6.

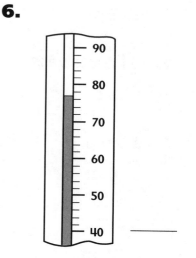

Teacher Note: Use after Quick Check page 256 to reteach Unit 10, Lesson 3. **(3)**

1 meter (m) = **100** centimeters
1 kilometer (km) = **1,000** meters

The width of your thumb is about
1 centimeter.

The width of a door is about **1 meter**.

You can walk **1 kilometer** in about **15** minutes.

Measure to the nearest centimeter.

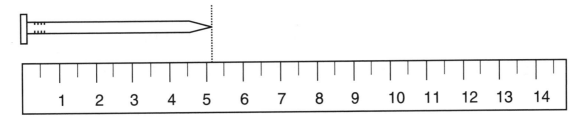

Find the centimeter marks that the end of the nail is between.
Think: It is between **5** and **6**.

Write the mark it is closer to. It is closer to **5** cm.

Measure to the nearest centimeter.

1.

Think:
Closer to 10 cm

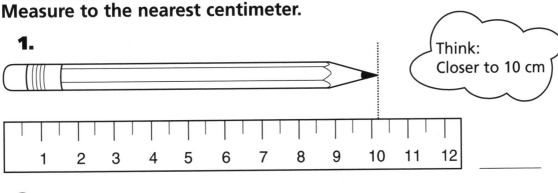

2.

Loop the best unit for measuring.

3. the length of an airplane

    cm   m   km

4. the length of a key

    cm   m   km

5. the distance of a bus ride

    cm   m   km

6. the length of a worm

    cm   m   km

Teacher Note: Use after Quick Check page 264 to reteach Unit 10, Lesson 5. **(3)**

Mass	**Liquid Measures**

The mass of a nickel is about **5 grams (g)**.

The mass of a backpack is about **5 kilograms (kg)**.

The thimble holds about **3 milliliters (mL)** of water.

The pot holds about **3 liters (L)** of water.

Loop the better estimate of mass.

1. an apple

90 g   900 kg

2. a crayon

3 g   3 kg

3. a puppy

10 kg   100 kg

4. a paper clip

1 g   100 g

5. a brick

1 g   1 kg

6. an eraser

10 g   2 kg

Loop the more reasonable liquid measure for the object.

7. a carton of milk

1 L   10 mL

8. a teakettle

2 L   20 mL

9. a glass of water

100 mL   10 L

10. a bathtub of water

100 mL   100 L

11. a test tube

10 mL   1 L

12. a juice box

200 mL   20 L

Teacher Note: Use after Quick Check page 264 to reteach Unit 10, Lesson 6. **(3)**

Each mark on the thermometer is **1°C** more than the mark below it.

To read the **Celsius** thermometer, read across from the top of the liquid to the number on the thermometer.

The liquid is **3** marks above **25°**. You can count from **25**: **25°, 26°, 27°, 28°**.

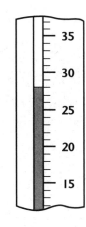

The thermometer shows a temperature of **28°C**.

Use the thermometer to write the temperature.

1.

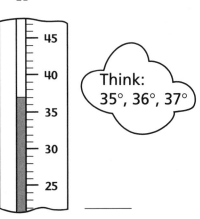

Think: 35°, 36°, 37°

_____

2.

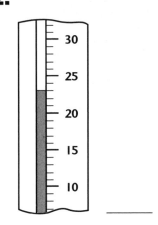

_____

3.

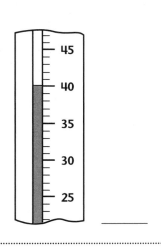

_____

4.

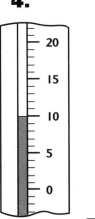

_____

5.

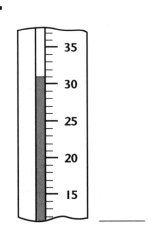

_____

6.

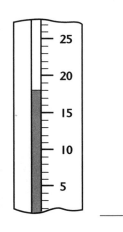

_____

Teacher Note: Use after Quick Check page 264 to reteach Unit 10, Lesson 7. **(3)**

Perimeter is the distance around a figure.
Find the perimeter of the rectangle.

Add the measures of the sides:

3 + 6 + 3 + 6 = 18

The perimeter is **18** ft.

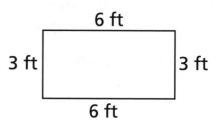

Find the perimeter.

1.

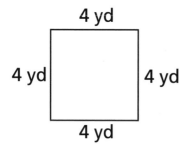

_____ yd

2.

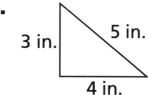

_____ in.

3.

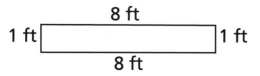

_____ ft

4.

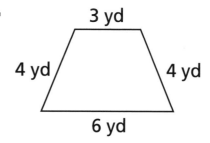

_____ yd

5.

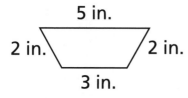

_____ in.

6.

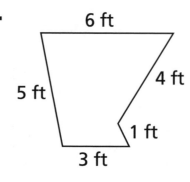

_____ ft

Teacher Note: Use after Quick Check page 272 to reteach Unit 10, Lesson 8. **(3)**

Area is the amount of surface covered by a figure. It is measured in square units.

Find the area of the shaded figure.

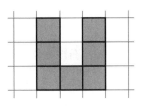

Count the number of squares. There are **7** squares.

The area is **7** square units.

Find the area.

1.

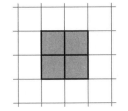

Count **4** squares.

_____ square units

2.

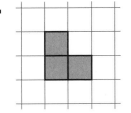

Count **3** squares.

_____ square units

3.

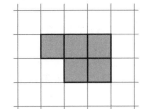

Count **5** squares.

_____ square units

4.

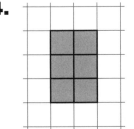

_____ square units

5.

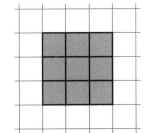

_____ square units

6.

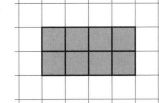

_____ square units

7.

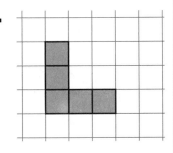

_____ square units

8.

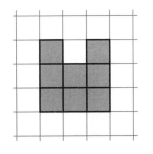

_____ square units

9.

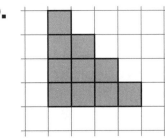

_____ square units

Teacher Note: Use after Quick Check page 272 to reteach Unit 10, Lesson 9. **(3)**

Volume is the measure of the space inside a container or solid.

Volume is measured in cubic units.

Find the volume of this solid.

Count the number of cubes. There are **4** cubes in the front and **4** cubes in the back. Some of the cubes in the back are hidden.

The volume is **8** cubic units.

Find the volume. Remember, some cubes may be hidden.

1.

Count **3** cubes.

_____ cubic units

2.

Count **4** cubes.

_____ cubic units

3.

Count **4** cubes.

_____ cubic units

4.

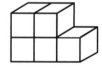

_____ cubic units

5.

_____ cubic units

6.

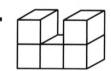

_____ cubic units

7.

_____ cubic units

8.

_____ cubic units

9.

_____ cubic units

Teacher Note: Use after Quick Check page 272 to reteach Unit 10, Lesson 11. **(3)**

How many?

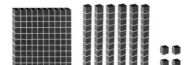

Hundreds	Tens	Ones
1	6	4

Write the number in standard form: **164.**

Compare:

12 = 10 + 2

12 is equal to **10 + 2**

27 < 31

27 is less than **31**

23 > 19

23 is greater than **19**

Write the number in standard form.

1.

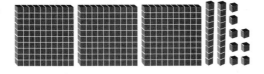

_____

2.

_____

3.

Hundreds	Tens	Ones
4	1	7

_____

4.

Hundreds	Tens	Ones
6	2	8

_____

Compare. Choose >, <, or =.

5.

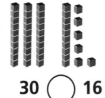

30 ◯ 16

6. 11 ◯ 20

7. 24 ◯ 20 + 4

8. 32 ◯ 28

9. 15 ◯ 19

10. 209 ◯ 290

11. 156 ◯ 165

12. 321 ◯ 331

13. 407 ◯ 410

Teacher Note: Use before Unit 11, Lesson 1. **(3)**

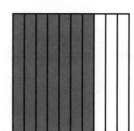

The model shows *four tenths* are shaded.

Write **4** tenths or $\frac{4}{10}$ or **0.4**.

The model shows *seven tenths* are shaded.

Write **7** tenths or $\frac{7}{10}$ or **0.7**.

0.4 and **0.7** are **decimals**.

Write the decimal.

1.

_____

2.

_____

3.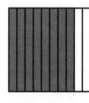

_____

4.

_____

5.

_____

6.

_____

7. 9 tenths

_____

8. 3 tenths

_____

9. 4 tenths

_____

10. 1 tenth

_____

11. 8 tenths

_____

12. 2 tenths

_____

13. $\frac{7}{10}$

_____

14. $\frac{9}{10}$

_____

15. $\frac{6}{10}$

_____

Teacher Note: Use after Quick Check page 284 to reteach Unit 11, Lesson 1. **(3)**

The decimal model shows that *three* and *six tenths* are shaded.

Write **3 $\frac{6}{10}$** or **3.6** or three and six tenths.

You can show the number in a place-value chart:

Ones		Tenths
3	.	6

Write the decimal.

1.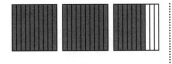

_____

2.

_____

3.

_____

4.
Ones		Tenths
6	.	5

_____

5.
Ones		Tenths
0	.	7

_____

6.
Ones		Tenths
4	.	8

_____

7. 4 $\frac{9}{10}$

_____

8. 1 $\frac{3}{10}$

_____

9. $\frac{2}{10}$

_____

10. 7 $\frac{1}{10}$

_____

11. 9 $\frac{5}{10}$

_____

12. 6 $\frac{4}{10}$

_____

13. three and five tenths

_____

14. eight and two tenths

_____

15. twelve and six tenths

_____

16. six and one tenth

_____

17. two and three tenths

_____

18. five and nine tenths

_____

Teacher Note: Use after Quick Check page 284 to reteach Unit 11, Lesson 2. **(3)**

The model shows that *forty-two hundredths* are shaded.

Write **42** hundredths

or $\frac{42}{100}$ or **0.42**.

The model shows that *eighty hundredths* are shaded.

Write **80** hundredths

or $\frac{80}{100}$ or **0.80**.

The model shows that *six hundredths* are shaded.

Write six hundredths

or $\frac{6}{100}$ or **0.06**.

Write the decimal.

1.

_____

2.

_____

3.

_____

4.

_____

5.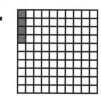

_____

6.

_____

7. 64 hundredths

_____

8. 50 hundredths

_____

9. 33 hundredths

_____

10. 11 hundredths

_____

11. 85 hundredths

_____

12. 2 hundredths

_____

13. $\frac{75}{100}$

_____

14. $\frac{94}{100}$

_____

15. $\frac{43}{100}$

_____

Teacher Note: Use after Quick Check page 284 to reteach Unit 11, Lesson 3. **(3)**

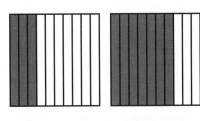

3 tenths is less than **7** tenths
0.3 < 0.7

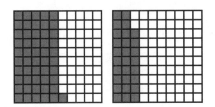

51 hundredths is greater than **28** hundredths

0.51 > 0.28

Compare. Choose >, <, or =.

1.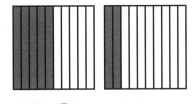

0.5 ◯ 0.2

2.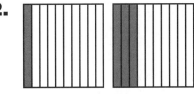

0.1 ◯ 0.3

3.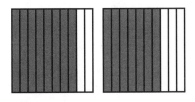

0.8 ◯ 0.7

4.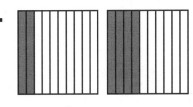

0.2 ◯ 0.4

5.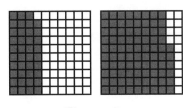

0.39 ◯ 0.86

6.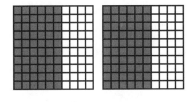

0.60 ◯ 0.60

7. 0.2 ◯ 0.1

8. 0.9 ◯ 0.6

9. 0.93 ◯ 0.59

10. 0.15 ◯ 0.30

Teacher Note: Use after Quick Check page 290 to reteach Unit 11, Lesson 4. **(3)**

Add or subtract decimals the same way as with whole
numbers. Just remember to line up the decimal points.

Add: **19.3 + 14.2**

Tens	Ones	.	Tenths
1	9	.	3
1	4	.	2
3	3	.	5

(+)

First add the tenths, then
the ones, then the tens.

Subtract: **29.8 − 14.5**

Tens	Ones	.	Tenths
2	9	.	8
1	4	.	5
1	5	.	3

(−)

First subtract the tenths, then
the ones, then the tens.

Add or subtract.

1.

Tens	Ones	.	Tenths
	3	.	3
	7	.	5
		.	8

(+)

2.

Tens	Ones	.	Tenths
	7	.	9
	5	.	1
		.	8

(−)

3.

Tens	Ones	.	Tenths
2	4	.	6
1	2	.	4
		.	

(+)

4.

Tens	Ones	.	Tenths
1	7	.	8
3	6	.	5
		.	

(+)

5.

Tens	Ones	.	Tenths
2	9	.	8
1	6	.	2
		.	

(−)

6.

Tens	Ones	.	Tenths
4	8	.	1
	5	.	3
		.	

(−)

7. 42.7 + 38.6

Tens	Ones	.	Tenths
		.	
		.	
		.	

(+)

8. 50.7 − 36.2

Tens	Ones	.	Tenths
		.	
		.	
		.	

(−)

Teacher Note: Use after Quick Check page 290 to reteach Unit 11, Lesson 6. (3)

Multiply and divide with money just as you do with
whole numbers. Remember to write the dollar sign
and the decimal point in the answer.

Multiply: **$1.63 × 2**

$$\begin{array}{r} 1 \\ \$1.63 \\ \times\ \ \ 2 \\ \hline \$3.26 \end{array}$$ ← Write the dollar sign
and the decimal point.

Divide: **$1.52 ÷ 4**

$$\begin{array}{r} \$\ .38 \\ 4)\overline{\$1.52} \\ -1\,2 \\ \hline 32 \\ -32 \\ \hline 0 \end{array}$$ ← Write the dollar sign
and decimal point.

**Multiply. Remember to write the dollar sign and
decimal point.**

1. $1.42
    × 4
   ⎯⎯⎯
    5 68

2. $2.36
    × 2
   ⎯⎯⎯
    4 72

3. $4.72
    × 3
   ⎯⎯⎯

4. $2.15
    × 6
   ⎯⎯⎯

5. $1.48
    × 8
   ⎯⎯⎯

6. $5.39
    × 3
   ⎯⎯⎯

7. $3.05
    × 5
   ⎯⎯⎯

8. $4.16
    × 2
   ⎯⎯⎯

**Divide. Remember to write the dollar sign and decimal
point.**

9. $3)\overline{\$2.58}$ (86)

10. $6)\overline{\$1.92}$ (32)

11. $4)\overline{\$2.12}$

12. $5)\overline{\$2.25}$

13. $8)\overline{\$2.96}$

14. $3)\overline{\$1.38}$

15. $6)\overline{\$2.46}$

16. $4)\overline{\$2.44}$

10 dimes = **1** dollar, so **1** dime is $\frac{1}{10}$ of a dollar.

10¢ = $.10 = $\frac{1}{10}$ of a dollar

60¢ = $.60 = $\frac{6}{10}$ of a dollar

4 quarters = **1** dollar, so **1** quarter is $\frac{1}{4}$ of a dollar.

If you divide the quarters into **2** equal groups, there will be **2** quarters in each group.

So, **2** quarters make $\frac{1}{2}$ of a dollar.

50¢ = $.50 = $\frac{1}{2}$ of a dollar

75¢ = $.75 = $\frac{3}{4}$ of a dollar

Use models to find the decimal and money amount.

1. What decimal tells $\frac{3}{10}$ of a dollar?   _.30_ $._____

2. What decimal tells $\frac{8}{10}$ of a dollar?   _____   _____

3. What decimal tells $\frac{7}{10}$ of a dollar?   _____   _____

4. What decimal tells $\frac{1}{4}$ of a dollar?   _____   _____

5. What decimal tells $\frac{1}{2}$ of a dollar?   _____   _____

Teacher Note: Use after Quick Check page 294 to reteach Unit 11, Lesson 8. **(3)**

Extension Worksheets

Extension Worksheets

NOTES

Think about the place value of each digit to
write the greatest or least number possible
from a list of numbers.

Write the greatest possible **5**-digit number using five of these digits	3 1 7 4 0 6

The greatest possible **5**-digit number is **76,431**.

**Write the greatest possible 4-digit number
using four of the digits in the box.**

1. | 9 5 1 8 2 |

2. | 6 4 3 7 3 |

_____   _____

Find the number.

3. Use **7, 4, 8, 3**. Use each digit
only once. Make the least
number possible.

_____

4. Use **6, 0, 3, 5, 1**. Use each
digit only once. Make the
greatest number possible.

_____

5. Use **8, 6, 3, 2, 5, 9**. Use each
digit only once. Make the
least number possible.

_____

6. Use **7, 3, 0, 4, 2, 5**. Use each
digit only once. Make the
greatest number possible.

_____

7. Use the digits **9, 3, 7, 2** only
once. Make the least number
that has **7** ones.

_____

8. Use the digits **3, 1, 5, 2, 4** only
once. Make the greatest
number that has **5** tens.

_____

9. Use the digits **2, 5, 6, 0** only
once. Make the least number
possible between **5,000** and
6,000.

_____

10. Use the digits **4, 7, 8, 3, 5** only
once. Make the greatest
number possible between
40,000 and **50,000**.

_____

Extension Worksheets

Use logical reasoning and the clues
to find the number.

The number is between **25** and **35**.
List all the possible numbers.

CLUES
It is between **25** and **35**.
It is not odd.
It does not have **2** tens.
The sum of the digits is **5**.

26	27	28	29	30	31	32	33	34

The number is not odd, so list only the even
numbers from above.

26	28	30	32	34

The number does not have a **2** in the tens
place, so remove **26** and **28** from the list.

		30	32	34

The sum of the digits is **5**. So, the number is **32**.

Use logical reasoning to solve each problem.

1. Kyle is thinking of a number
between **18** and **28**. It does not
have **5** ones. It is not even. The
number is not **19**. The sum of
the digits is greater than **5**.
What is the number?

_____

2. Shana is thinking of a number
between **400** and **500**. It has a
2 in the tens place. It is even.
The digit in the ones place is
less than **2**. What is the
number?

_____

3. What is Rick's number? It is
between **86** and **93**. It does
not have a **9** in the tens place
or the ones place. It is not
next to **86**.

_____

4. What is Jamie's number? It is
between **495** and **505**. It does
not have a **9** in the tens place.
It is not even. The digit in the
ones place is greater than **2**.

_____

5. Jeff is thinking of a capital
letter. It comes after Q in the
alphabet. It is not a vowel. It
has no straight lines. What is
the letter?

_____

6. Debbie is thinking of a letter.
It comes before K in the
alphabet. It is in the word
faithful but not in the word
calf. What is the letter?

_____

Teacher Note: Use after Unit 1, Lesson 10. **(3)**

Use **30, 70,** and **+** to build the numbers
120 and **130**.

$120 = 30 + 30 + 30 + 30$

$130 = 30 + 30 + 70$

Notice that you can use each number more
than once if you need to.

Use 30, 50, and +. Build the number.

1. 110 = _____

2. 120 = _____

3. 130 = _____

4. 140 = _____

5. 150 = _____

6. 160 = _____

7. 170 = _____

8. 180 = _____

9. 190 = _____

10. 200 = _____

**Use 40, 70, and +. Build as many numbers as
you can. Which two numbers cannot be
built?**

11. 110 = _____

12. 120 = _____

13. 130 = _____

14. 140 = _____

15. 150 = _____

16. 160 = _____

17. 170 = _____

18. 180 = _____

19. 190 = _____

20. 200 = _____

21. The two numbers that cannot be built are _____ and _____.

Extension Worksheets

Teacher Note: Use after Unit 2, Lesson 3. **(3)**

How many students
are in the chorus?

Students in Chorus	
Boys	Girls
8	19

You can do a problem like this in your head.
Use a simpler addition fact with the same digits
in the ones place.

$9 + 8 = 17$ This sum ends in a **7**.

Increase the tens
digit by **1**, since
$19 = 9 + 10$. $19 + 8 = 27$ So this sum must end in a **7**, too.

There are **27** students in the chorus.

Try these.
56 + 7 = ? $6 + 7 = 13$

so, **56 + 7 = 63**

39 + 9 = ? $9 + 9 = 18$

so, **39 + 9 = 48**

Use mental math to find the sum.

1. 45 + 6 = _____   **2.** 56 + 7 = _____   **3.** 16 + 3 = _____

4. 28 + 9 = _____   **5.** 39 + 6 = _____   **6.** 74 + 5 = _____

7. 69 + 3 = _____   **8.** 26 + 9 = _____   **9.** 17 + 8 = _____

10. 26 + 6 = _____   **11.** 42 + 9 = _____   **12.** 31 + 9 = _____

13. 37 + 5 = _____   **14.** 65 + 9 = _____   **15.** 34 + 8 = _____

16. 28 + 3 = _____   **17.** 47 + 7 = _____   **18.** 68 + 6 = _____

Teacher Note: Use after Unit 2, Lesson 4. (3)

How many more boys than girls
are in the band?

Students in Band	
Boys	Girls
46	29

You can do a problem like this in your head.
Notice that **29** ends in **9**. The next ten after
29 is **30**.

Think: **46 − 30 = 16**

Add back **1** since
29 + 1 = 30.   **16 + 1 = 17**
                    So: **46 − 29 = 17**

There are **17** more boys than girls in
the band.

Try these.

$$87 - 29 \qquad \text{Think: } 87 - 30 = 57 \qquad 57 + 1 = 58 \qquad \text{So: } \frac{87 - 29}{58}$$

$$62 - 39 \qquad \text{Think: } 62 - 40 = 22 \qquad 22 + 1 = 23 \qquad \text{So: } \frac{62 - 39}{23}$$

Use mental math to find the difference.

1. 45 − 19 = _____   **2.** 56 − 39 = _____   **3.** 86 − 69 = _____

4. 28 − 19 = _____   **5.** 72 − 29 = _____   **6.** 54 − 29 = _____

7. 64 − 29 = _____   **8.** 96 − 19 = _____   **9.** 97 − 39 = _____

10. 66 − 49 = _____   **11.** 92 − 69 = _____   **12.** 71 − 29 = _____

13. 37 − 19 = _____   **14.** 65 − 29 = _____   **15.** 94 − 29 = _____

16. 78 − 39 = _____   **17.** 47 − 19 = _____   **18.** 81 − 59 = _____

Extension Worksheets

Teacher Note: Use after Unit 3, Lesson 5. **(3)**

A **multiple** of a number is the product of that number and another number.

2 × 3 = 6
So **6** is a multiple of **2**.
It is also a multiple of **3**.

2 × 4 = 8
So **8** is a multiple of **2** and of **4**.

3 × 5 = 15
So **15** is a multiple of **3** and of **5**.

To find the multiples of a number, multiply the number by **1**, by **2**, by **3**, and so on.

The first **5** multiples of **2** are **2, 4, 6, 8**, and **10** because **2 × 1 = 2, 2 × 2 = 4, 2 × 3 = 6, 2 × 4 = 8**, and **2 × 5 = 10.**

Use the chart to complete the exercises.

1	2	3	4	5	6	7	8	9	10
11	12	13	14	15	16	17	18	19	20
21	22	23	24	25	26	27	28	29	30
31	32	33	34	35	36	37	38	39	40
41	42	43	44	45	46	47	48	49	50
51	52	53	54	55	56	57	58	59	60
61	62	63	64	65	66	67	68	69	70
71	72	73	74	75	76	77	78	79	80
81	82	83	84	85	86	87	88	89	90
91	92	93	94	95	96	97	98	99	100

1. Circle the multiples of **2** in red.

2. Circle the multiples of **3** in blue.

3. Circle the multiples of **4** in green.

4. Circle the multiples of **5** in yellow.

5. List all the multiples of **5**. What pattern do you see? _____

_____

6. What number is a multiple of **2, 3, 4,** and **5**? _____

7. What is the first number that is greater than **1**

and is not a multiple of **2, 3, 4,** or **5**? _____

8. Describe another pattern you see in the chart. _____

_____

Teacher Note: Use after Unit 4, Lesson 8. **(3)**

Here is a number machine.

A number goes in.
Something happens to it.
A different number comes out.

5 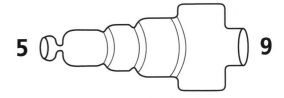 9

You can write a rule to describe
what happens to the IN number
to get the OUT number.

Look at the rules for this table.

IN	OUT
5	9
6	10
10	14
11	15

rule: Add **4**

Complete the table. Write the rule.

1.

IN	OUT
2	6
3	9
4	___
7	___

rule: Multiply by _____

2.

IN	OUT
1	6
2	7
5	___
6	___

rule: _____

3.

IN	OUT
10	1
11	2
12	___
15	___

rule: _____

4.

IN	OUT
4	8
5	10
6	___
9	___

rule: _____

5. Make your own IN/OUT machine and
table. Have a friend find the rule.

Extension Worksheets

Sort the polygons shown above into **2** different groups. Draw the figures. Label each group.

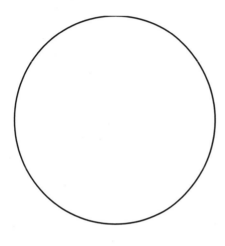 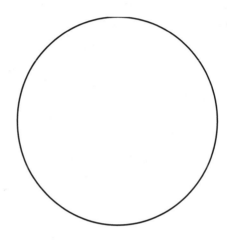

_____   _____

Sort the polygons another way. Think about which figures belong in both groups. Draw those figures in the part that overlaps.

Hint: You will not use all of the
polygons shown above.

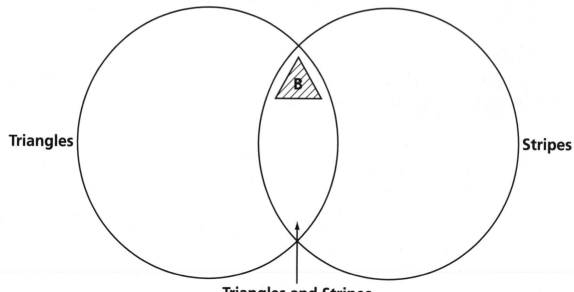

Triangles and Stripes

Teacher Note: Use after Unit 6, Lesson 1. **(3)**

Name _____

Some windows slide to open.

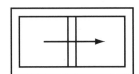

a slide

A mirror can show a flip image.

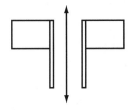

a flip

The flag is turned around a point.

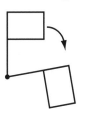

a turn

A slide, a flip, and a turn are ways that a figure can change position.

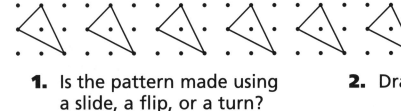

1. Is the pattern made using a slide, a flip, or a turn?

2. Draw the next shape.

_____

Draw the next shape in the pattern. Is it a slide, a flip, or a turn?

3.

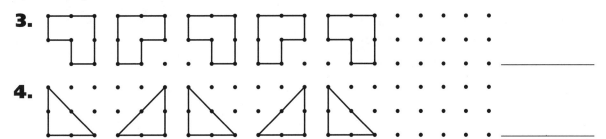

4.

_____

Teacher Note: Use after Unit 6, Lesson 5. **(3)**

The graph shows the typical weather in April at Vincenzo's Vacation Resort. Use the information in the graph to answer the questions.

1. The Ito Family is spending April at the resort. Should they pack an umbrella? Explain your answer.

_____

_____

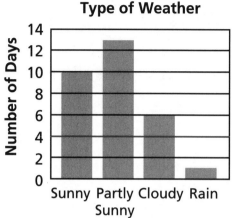

Type of Weather

2. Does the graph show if it will be warm enough to swim in the outdoor pool? Explain.

_____

3. What do you think the weather will be like the first day in May? Why do you think so?

_____

The graph shows the daily high temperature at Sky High Mountain Resort. Use the information in the graph to answer the questions.

4. The resort guarantees skiing when the temperature stays under **32°** for **3** or more days in a row. Are there any days this week when skiing is not guaranteed? Why or why not?

_____

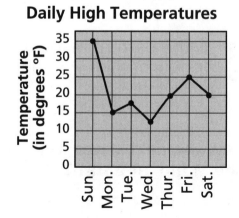

Daily High Temperatures

5. What do you think will happen to the temperature during the following two weeks? Why do you think so?

_____

Teacher Note: Use after Unit 6, Lesson 12. **(3)**

Use the ruler above each question to answer the question.

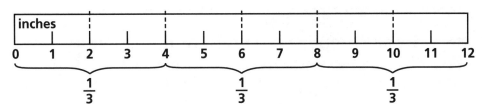

1. How many inches is $\frac{1}{3}$ of a foot? _____; $\frac{2}{3}$ of a foot? _____

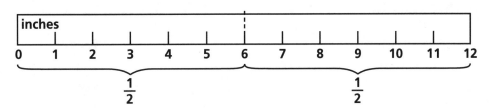

2. How many inches is $\frac{1}{2}$ of a foot? _____

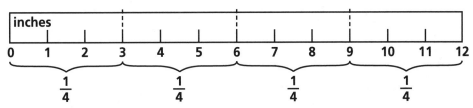

3. How many inches is $\frac{1}{4}$ of a foot? _____; $\frac{3}{4}$ of a foot? _____

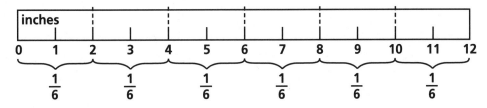

4. How many inches is $\frac{1}{6}$ of a foot? _____; $\frac{5}{6}$ of a foot? _____

Complete. Use the rulers above to help you.

5. $\frac{1}{2}$ of a foot = $\frac{\square}{4}$ a foot. **6.** $\frac{2}{3}$ of a foot = $\frac{\square}{6}$ of a foot.

7. $\frac{1}{2}$ of a foot = $\frac{\square}{6}$ of a foot. **8.** $\frac{1}{3}$ of a foot = $\frac{\square}{6}$ of a foot.

Teacher Note: Use after Unit 7, Lesson 4. **(3)**

The kids club lost their code. Can you help them figure it out?

| **Code Clues** |
| Each different object represents a different number. |
| Each same object represents the same number. |

Find a number for each shape so that all the exercises are correct. Write the number sentence.

1. ▲ + ▲ = 10 _____   ▲ = ____

▲ + ● = 9 _____   ● = ____

● + ■ = 5 _____   ■ = ____

◆ + ● + ● = 10 _____   ◆ = ____

▲ + ● + ■ = ★ _____   ★ = ____

Find a number for each object so that all the exercises are correct. Write the number sentence.

| **Think:** What operation is used? +, −, × ÷ |

2. 🍎 × 🍎 = 16 _____   🍎 = ____

🍌 × 🍎 = 12 _____   🍌 = ____

🍌 × 🍐 = 15 _____   🍐 = ____

🍐 × 🍇 = 🍐 _____   🍇 = ____

Assign each object a number so that both sentences are true.

3. ♡ + ⬆ = ◇   ⬆ − ♡ = 🐟   ♡ = ____   ⬆ = ____   🐟 = ____

Assign each object a number so that both sentences are true.

4. □ × △ = ○   ○ ÷ △ = □   □ = ____   △ = ____   ○ = ____

Teacher Note: Use after Unit 8, Lesson 2. **(3)**

Use 2, 3, 7, and ×.
Build the numbers using the numbers and operation given. You can use numbers more than once.

1. 14 = _____

2. 21 = _____

3. 28 = _____

4. 42 = _____

5. 56 = _____

6. 63 = _____

Use 3, 5, 7, and ×.

7. 15 = _____

8. 35 = _____

9. 45 = _____

10. 49 = _____

Use 2, 3, 5, and ×.

11. 4 = _____

12. 6 = _____

13. 8 = _____

14. 10 = _____

15. 12 = _____

16. 15 = _____

17. 16 = _____

18. 18 = _____

19. 20 = _____

20. 24 = _____

21. 25 = _____

22. 27 = _____

23. 30 = _____

24. 36 = _____

Extension Worksheets

Estimate with tens.

If mowing half of the lawn takes **26** minutes, about
how many minutes will it take to mow the entire lawn?

$$26 \text{ rounds to} \rightarrow 30$$
$$\underline{\times 2} \qquad\qquad \underline{\times 2}$$
$$\blacksquare \qquad\qquad 60$$

It will take about **60** minutes to mow the entire lawn.

Estimate with hundreds.	Estimate with money.
For hundreds, round to the nearest hundred to estimate.	If one treat costs **$.29**, about how much do **4** treats cost?

$174 \text{ rounds to} \rightarrow 200$	$\$.29 \text{ rounds to} \rightarrow \$.30$
$\underline{\times 4} \qquad\qquad \underline{\times 4}$	
$\blacksquare \qquad\qquad 800$	$4 \times \$.30 = \$1.20$

The treats cost about **$1.20.**

Estimate the product.

1. $28 \rightarrow 30$ **2.** 39 **3.** 22 **4.** 13
$\underline{\times 3} \quad \underline{\times 3}$ $\underline{\times 2} \quad \underline{\times}$ $\underline{\times 4} \quad \underline{\times}$ $\underline{\times 5} \quad \underline{\times}$
$\blacksquare$ $\blacksquare$ $\blacksquare$ $\blacksquare$

5. $324 \rightarrow 300$ **6.** 168 **7.** 291 **8.** 114
$\underline{\times 2} \quad \underline{\times 2}$ $\underline{\times 4} \quad \underline{\times}$ $\underline{\times 3} \quad \underline{\times}$ $\underline{\times 6} \quad \underline{\times}$

$\blacksquare$ $\blacksquare$ $\blacksquare$ $\blacksquare$

9. $4 \times \$.17$ **10.** $2 \times \$.52$ **11.** $5 \times \$.31$ **12.** $3 \times \$.28$

_____   _____   _____   _____

**Read each problem. Do you need to find an exact
or an approximate solution? Solve the problem.**

13. It takes Kevin **12** minutes to jog **1** mile. About how long will it take him to jog **4** miles?

_____

14. The bakery sells one muffin for **$.38**. About how much will half a dozen muffins cost?

_____

Teacher Note: Use after Unit 9, Lesson 7. **(3)**

Use 28, 34, 37	Test Each Number (by circling groups)			or Divide	Number(s)
Does the number when put in groups of **3** have **1** left over?	**28**	**34**	**37**	**28 ÷ 3 = 9 R1** **34 ÷ 3 = 11 R1** **37 ÷ 3 = 12 R1**	**28**, Yes **34**, Yes **37**, Yes
Does the number when put in groups of **4** have **1** left over?	**28**	**34**	**37**	28 ÷ 4 = _____ 34 ÷ 4 = _____ 37 ÷ 4 = _____	28, _____ 34, _____ 37, _____
Does the number when put in groups of **5** have **2** left over?	**28**	**34**	**37**	28 ÷ 5 = _____ 34 ÷ 5 = _____ 37 ÷ 5 = _____	28, _____ 34, _____ 37, _____

1. Complete the chart above.

2. Which number has a *yes* in each row? _____

Use the numbers: 44, 27, 36. Which numbers fit the given situation?

3. When put in **3** groups **2** is left over.　　_____

When put in **4** groups **0** is left over.　　_____

When put in **5** groups **4** is left over.　　_____

Which number fits every situation?　　_____

4. When put in **3** groups **0** is left over.　　_____

When put in **4** groups **0** is left over.　　_____

When put in **5** groups **1** is left over.　　_____

Which number fits every situation?　　_____

5. Can the number left over ever be larger than the number of groups? Explain your answer. _____

Extension Worksheets

Teacher Note: Use after Unit 9, Lesson 9. **(3)**

Estimate **115 ÷ 4.**

Think: **4 × ☐ = 115.**

Use what you know about basic facts.

4 × 1 = 4, so **4 × 10 = 40**

4 × 2 = 8, so **4 × 20 = 80** ←⎤ **115** is between **80** and **120,**
                                  but it is closer to **120.**
4 × 3 = 12, so **4 × 30 = 120** ←⎦ So, **115 ÷ 4** is about **30.**

Complete the multiplication equations. Then estimate the quotient.

1. 2 × 3 = ____ so, 2 × 30 = ____   **2.** 3 × 5 = 15 so, 3 × 50 = 150

   2 × 4 = ____ so, 2 × 40 = ____   3 × 6 = 18 so, 3 × 60 = 180

   63 ÷ 2 is about _____.   176 ÷ 3 is about _____.

Circle the letter of the better estimate.

3. 87 ÷ 3   **4.** 124 ÷ 2   **5.** 78 ÷ 4   **6.** 142 ÷ 5

  a. 20   a. 50   a. 20   a. 30

  b. 30   b. 60   b. 30   b. 40

Estimate the quotient.

7. 63 ÷ 2   **8.** 76 ÷ 5   **9.** 52 ÷ 5   **10.** 82 ÷ 4

  _____   _____   _____   _____

11. 29 ÷ 3   **12.** 43 ÷ 2   **13.** 58 ÷ 2   **14.** 61 ÷ 3

  _____   _____   _____   _____

15. 122 ÷ 6   **16.** 145 ÷ 5   **17.** 245 ÷ 8   **18.** 143 ÷ 7

  _____   _____   _____   _____

19. 168 ÷ 4   **20.** 182 ÷ 6   **21.** 139 ÷ 2   **22.** 158 ÷ 5

  _____   _____   _____   _____

Teacher Note: Use after Unit 9, Lesson 11. **(3)**

The ruler shown below can be used to measure to the nearest inch, half inch, or quarter inch.

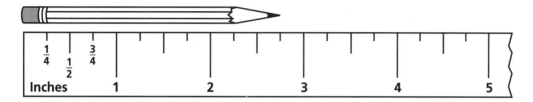

The pencil is $2\frac{3}{4}$ inches long.

Find objects in your classroom that you estimate are about 5 inches long. Then use the ruler to measure each object to the nearest quarter inch.

	Object	Length
1.		
2.		
3.		
4.		
5.		
6.		

Complete.

7. How did you estimate that an object was

about **5** inches long? _____

_____

_____

8. When would it be helpful to measure length to the nearest quarter inch? Give an example.

_____

_____

Teacher Note: Use after Unit 10, Lesson 1. (3)

Estimate the area.

Count the number of whole squares.
There are **14** whole squares.

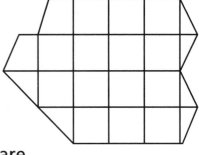

Then count the number of almost whole
squares, half squares, and quarter squares.

There are **2** almost whole squares.
There are **2** half squares or about **1** whole square.
There are **4** quarter squares or about **1** whole square.

Add to estimate the area: **14 + 2 + 1 + 1 = 18**
The area is about **18** square units.

Estimate the area.

1.

about _____
square units

2.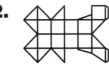

about _____
square units

3.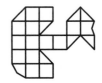

about _____
square units

4. Trace part of your hand on the grid.
Estimate the area of your hand.

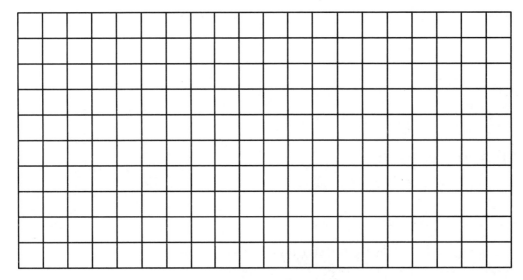

about _____ square units

Teacher Note: Use after Unit 10, Lesson 9. **(3)**

You can use a number line to round decimals to the nearest whole number.

Round **12.4** to the nearest whole number.

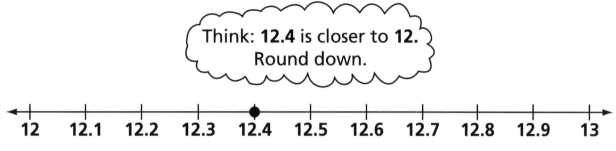

Think: **12.4** is closer to **12**.
Round down.

So, **12.4** rounded to the nearest whole number is **12**.

You can also round decimals without a number line.

> **Remember**
> If the digit is **5** or greater, round up to the next tenth.
>
> If the digit is less than **5**, round down.

Round **5.37** to the nearest tenth.

Look at the digit in the hundredths place.

Think: **7 > 5**. Round up.

So **5.37** rounded to the nearest tenth is **5.4**.

Round to the nearest whole number.

1. 7.2 _____	**2.** 18.1 _____	**3.** 43.7 _____
4. 26.6 _____	**5.** 4.3 _____	**6.** 10.9 _____
7. 93.3 _____	**8.** 1.6 _____	**9.** 36.4 _____
10. 78.4 _____	**11.** 62.8 _____	**12.** 58.6 _____

Round to the nearest tenth.

13. 2.34 _____	**14.** 4.29 _____	**15.** 10.52 _____
16. 5.46 _____	**17.** 0.83 _____	**18.** 7.66 _____
19. 9.83 _____	**20.** 24.52 _____	**21.** 0.69 _____
22. 15.68 _____	**23.** 39.27 _____	**24.** 43.08 _____

Teacher Note: Use after Unit 11, Lesson 3. **(3)**

Name _____

1. Complete the number line by filling in the
missing decimals and fractions.

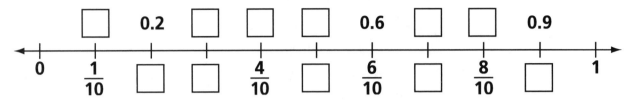

2. Locate and label the decimals **0.1, 0.5, 0.7,**
and **0.9** on the number line.

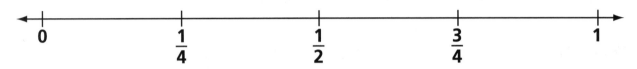

3. Locate and label the decimals **0.2, 0.4, 0.6,**
and **0.8** on the number line.

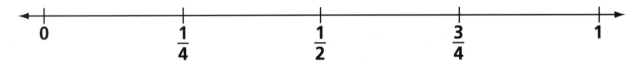

4. Locate and label the fractions $\frac{1}{4}$, $\frac{1}{2}$, and $\frac{3}{4}$
on the number line.

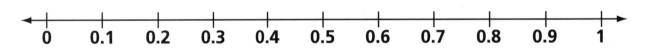

**Write >, <, or =. Use your number lines above
to help.**

5. $\frac{3}{4} \bigcirc \frac{1}{4}$

6. $\frac{1}{4} \bigcirc \frac{1}{2}$

7. 0.6 $\bigcirc$ 0.8

8. 0.4 $\bigcirc$ 0.2

9. $\frac{8}{10} \bigcirc$ 0.8

10. $\frac{3}{4} \bigcirc$ 0.6

11. 1 $\bigcirc$ 0.3

12. 0.4 $\bigcirc \frac{1}{2}$

13. $\frac{2}{4} \bigcirc$ 0.9

Teacher Note: Use after Unit 11, Lesson 4. **(3)**

Teaching Resources

Teaching Resources

Unit _____ Cumulative Review

Mark the space for the answer you have chosen.

1. Ⓐ Ⓑ Ⓒ Ⓓ Ⓔ
2. Ⓕ Ⓖ Ⓗ Ⓙ Ⓚ
3. Ⓐ Ⓑ Ⓒ Ⓓ Ⓔ
4. Ⓕ Ⓖ Ⓗ Ⓙ Ⓚ
5. Ⓐ Ⓑ Ⓒ Ⓓ Ⓔ
6. Ⓕ Ⓖ Ⓗ Ⓙ Ⓚ
7. Ⓐ Ⓑ Ⓒ Ⓓ Ⓔ
8. Ⓕ Ⓖ Ⓗ Ⓙ Ⓚ
9. Ⓐ Ⓑ Ⓒ Ⓓ Ⓔ
10. Ⓕ Ⓖ Ⓗ Ⓙ Ⓚ
11. Ⓐ Ⓑ Ⓒ Ⓓ Ⓔ
12. Ⓕ Ⓖ Ⓗ Ⓙ Ⓚ
13. Ⓐ Ⓑ Ⓒ Ⓓ Ⓔ
14. Ⓕ Ⓖ Ⓗ Ⓙ Ⓚ
15. Ⓐ Ⓑ Ⓒ Ⓓ Ⓔ
16. Ⓕ Ⓖ Ⓗ Ⓙ Ⓚ

Teaching Resources

Mark the space for the answer you have chosen.

1. Ⓐ Ⓑ Ⓒ Ⓓ Ⓔ		31. Ⓐ Ⓑ Ⓒ Ⓓ Ⓔ
2. Ⓕ Ⓖ Ⓗ Ⓙ Ⓚ		32. Ⓕ Ⓖ Ⓗ Ⓙ Ⓚ
3. Ⓐ Ⓑ Ⓒ Ⓓ Ⓔ		33. Ⓐ Ⓑ Ⓒ Ⓓ Ⓔ
4. Ⓕ Ⓖ Ⓗ Ⓙ Ⓚ		34. Ⓕ Ⓖ Ⓗ Ⓙ Ⓚ
5. Ⓐ Ⓑ Ⓒ Ⓓ Ⓔ		35. Ⓐ Ⓑ Ⓒ Ⓓ Ⓔ
6. Ⓕ Ⓖ Ⓗ Ⓙ Ⓚ		36. Ⓕ Ⓖ Ⓗ Ⓙ Ⓚ
7. Ⓐ Ⓑ Ⓒ Ⓓ Ⓔ		37. Ⓐ Ⓑ Ⓒ Ⓓ Ⓔ
8. Ⓕ Ⓖ Ⓗ Ⓙ Ⓚ		38. Ⓕ Ⓖ Ⓗ Ⓙ Ⓚ
9. Ⓐ Ⓑ Ⓒ Ⓓ Ⓔ		39. Ⓐ Ⓑ Ⓒ Ⓓ Ⓔ
10. Ⓕ Ⓖ Ⓗ Ⓙ Ⓚ		40. Ⓕ Ⓖ Ⓗ Ⓙ Ⓚ
11. Ⓐ Ⓑ Ⓒ Ⓓ Ⓔ		41. Ⓐ Ⓑ Ⓒ Ⓓ Ⓔ
12. Ⓕ Ⓖ Ⓗ Ⓙ Ⓚ		42. Ⓕ Ⓖ Ⓗ Ⓙ Ⓚ
13. Ⓐ Ⓑ Ⓒ Ⓓ Ⓔ		43. Ⓐ Ⓑ Ⓒ Ⓓ Ⓔ
14. Ⓕ Ⓖ Ⓗ Ⓙ Ⓚ		44. Ⓕ Ⓖ Ⓗ Ⓙ Ⓚ
15. Ⓐ Ⓑ Ⓒ Ⓓ Ⓔ		45. Ⓐ Ⓑ Ⓒ Ⓓ Ⓔ
16. Ⓕ Ⓖ Ⓗ Ⓙ Ⓚ		46. Ⓕ Ⓖ Ⓗ Ⓙ Ⓚ
17. Ⓐ Ⓑ Ⓒ Ⓓ Ⓔ		47. Ⓐ Ⓑ Ⓒ Ⓓ Ⓔ
18. Ⓕ Ⓖ Ⓗ Ⓙ Ⓚ		48. Ⓕ Ⓖ Ⓗ Ⓙ Ⓚ
19. Ⓐ Ⓑ Ⓒ Ⓓ Ⓔ		49. Ⓐ Ⓑ Ⓒ Ⓓ Ⓔ
20. Ⓕ Ⓖ Ⓗ Ⓙ Ⓚ		50. Ⓕ Ⓖ Ⓗ Ⓙ Ⓚ
21. Ⓐ Ⓑ Ⓒ Ⓓ Ⓔ		51. Ⓐ Ⓑ Ⓒ Ⓓ Ⓔ
22. Ⓕ Ⓖ Ⓗ Ⓙ Ⓚ		52. Ⓕ Ⓖ Ⓗ Ⓙ Ⓚ
23. Ⓐ Ⓑ Ⓒ Ⓓ Ⓔ		53. Ⓐ Ⓑ Ⓒ Ⓓ Ⓔ
24. Ⓕ Ⓖ Ⓗ Ⓙ Ⓚ		54. Ⓕ Ⓖ Ⓗ Ⓙ Ⓚ
25. Ⓐ Ⓑ Ⓒ Ⓓ Ⓔ		55. Ⓐ Ⓑ Ⓒ Ⓓ Ⓔ
26. Ⓕ Ⓖ Ⓗ Ⓙ Ⓚ		56. Ⓕ Ⓖ Ⓗ Ⓙ Ⓚ
27. Ⓐ Ⓑ Ⓒ Ⓓ Ⓔ		57. Ⓐ Ⓑ Ⓒ Ⓓ Ⓔ
28. Ⓕ Ⓖ Ⓗ Ⓙ Ⓚ		58. Ⓕ Ⓖ Ⓗ Ⓙ Ⓚ
29. Ⓐ Ⓑ Ⓒ Ⓓ Ⓔ		59. Ⓐ Ⓑ Ⓒ Ⓓ Ⓔ
30. Ⓕ Ⓖ Ⓗ Ⓙ Ⓚ		60. Ⓕ Ⓖ Ⓗ Ⓙ Ⓚ

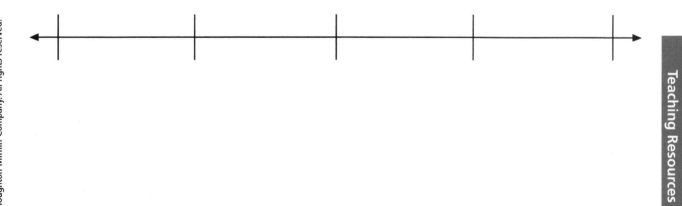

Teaching Resources

Thousands			Ones		
hundreds	tens	ones	hundreds	tens	ones

_____

_____

_____

_____

_____

_____

_____

_____

_____

Teaching Resources

1	2	3	4	5	6	7	8	9	10
11	12	13	14	15	16	17	18	19	20
21	22	23	24	25	26	27	28	29	30
31	32	33	34	35	36	37	38	39	40
41	42	43	44	45	46	47	48	49	50
51	52	53	54	55	56	57	58	59	60
61	62	63	64	65	66	67	68	69	70
71	72	73	74	75	76	77	78	79	80
81	82	83	84	85	86	87	88	89	90
91	92	93	94	95	96	97	98	99	100

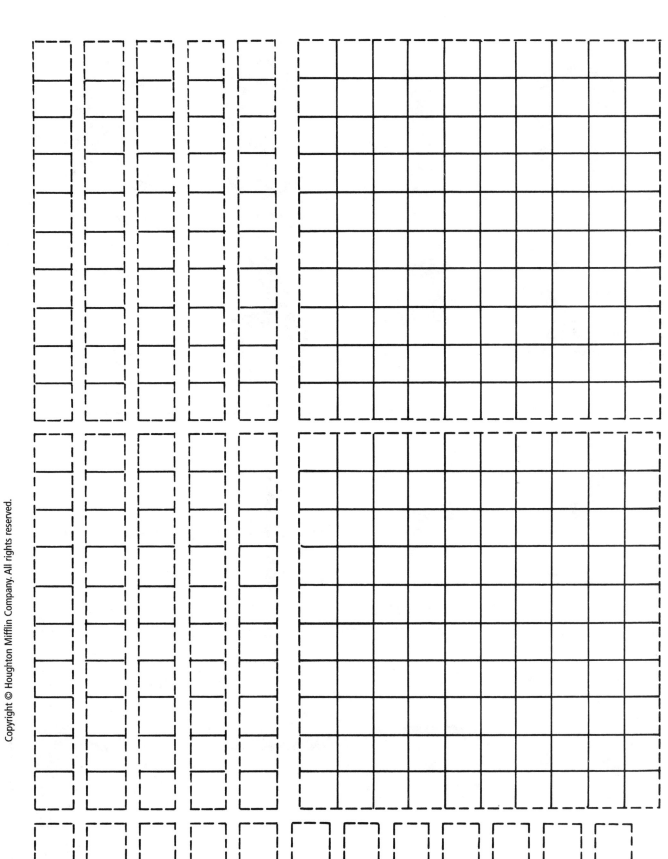

Teaching Resources

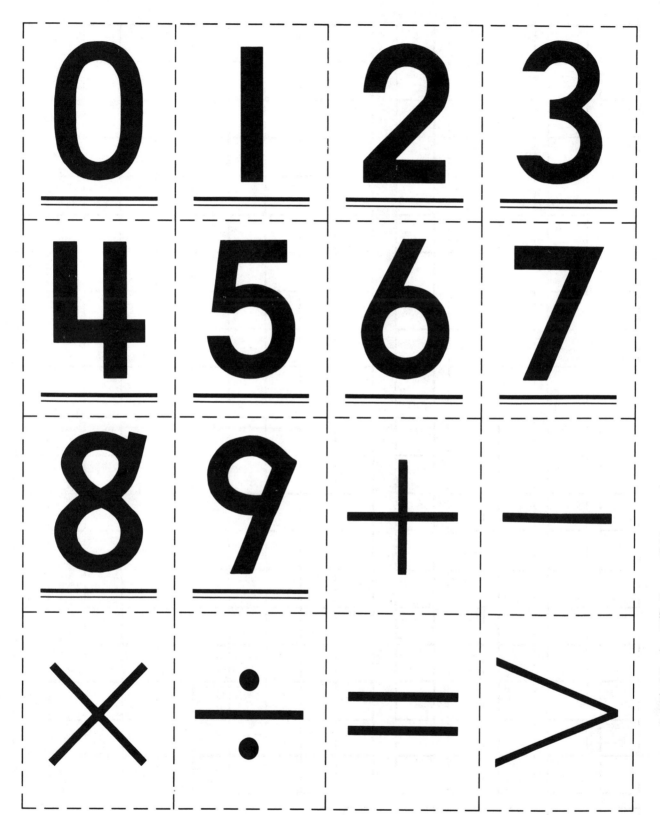

7 +6	9 +6	8 +5	9 +9	10 +5
5 +9	8 +6	8 +8	11 +8	12 +7
5 +8	9 +8	9 +5	10 +9	11 +7
7 +9	12 +5	11 +9	10 +8	6 +9
8 +9	10 +7	11 +6	8 +7	10 +10

Teaching Resources

+	0	1	2	3	4	5	6	7	8	9
0										
1										
2										
3										
4										
5										
6										
7										
8										
9										

13 −9	14 −7	17 −9	19 −9	15 −9	18 −11
17 −10	19 −8	18 −6	17 −11	18 −8	19 −12
19 −7	16 −7	13 −8	18 −9	14 −6	13 −5
13 −7	16 −5	15 −8	14 −8	18 −7	19 −10
14 −5	17 −8	13 −4	15 −7	16 −9	15 −5
19 −11	15 −6	16 −8	20 −10	14 −9	13 −6

5 ×2	2 ×3	4 ×0	3 ×3	2 ×4	4 ×8
3 ×4	5 ×6	4 ×4	3 ×2	5 ×5	4 ×3
4 ×2	1 ×6	2 ×5	5 ×4	2 ×6	3 ×5
4 ×5	2 ×7	5 ×9	3 ×6	5 ×8	4 ×9
3 ×7	4 ×6	5 ×3	2 ×8	3 ×8	0 ×7
2 ×9	5 ×7	4 ×1	1 ×9	4 ×7	3 ×9

8 $\times 2$	6 $\times 3$	8 $\times 8$	7 $\times 0$	8 $\times 5$	7 $\times 2$
6 $\times 4$	7 $\times 6$	9 $\times 2$	6 $\times 8$	9 $\times 9$	9 $\times 5$
9 $\times 3$	6 $\times 9$	7 $\times 3$	8 $\times 4$	6 $\times 1$	9 $\times 8$
7 $\times 5$	8 $\times 6$	6 $\times 2$	7 $\times 7$	9 $\times 7$	8 $\times 9$
8 $\times 1$	6 $\times 6$	9 $\times 4$	7 $\times 8$	9 $\times 6$	6 $\times 5$
8 $\times 7$	7 $\times 9$	6 $\times 7$	8 $\times 3$	9 $\times 0$	7 $\times 4$

Teaching Resources

	0	1	2	3	4	5	6	7	8	9	10
0											
1											
2											
3											
4											
5											
6											
7											
8											
9											
10											

$5\overline{)40}$	$3\overline{)24}$	$5\overline{)45}$	$3\overline{)3}$	$5\overline{)20}$	$3\overline{)6}$
$3\overline{)15}$	$2\overline{)18}$	$4\overline{)36}$	$4\overline{)12}$	$2\overline{)4}$	$4\overline{)20}$
$2\overline{)10}$	$4\overline{)4}$	$5\overline{)30}$	$3\overline{)21}$	$5\overline{)35}$	$2\overline{)16}$
$4\overline{)24}$	$5\overline{)5}$	$2\overline{)12}$	$4\overline{)32}$	$2\overline{)14}$	$5\overline{)15}$
$2\overline{)2}$	$3\overline{)12}$	$4\overline{)8}$	$5\overline{)10}$	$3\overline{)9}$	$2\overline{)6}$
$5\overline{)25}$	$4\overline{)28}$	$2\overline{)8}$	$3\overline{)18}$	$4\overline{)16}$	$3\overline{)27}$

Teaching Resources

$6\overline{)24}$	$9\overline{)81}$	$8\overline{)56}$	$9\overline{)36}$	$8\overline{)64}$	$7\overline{)35}$
$7\overline{)63}$	$8\overline{)32}$	$6\overline{)48}$	$7\overline{)7}$	$6\overline{)18}$	$8\overline{)40}$
$9\overline{)9}$	$7\overline{)28}$	$8\overline{)8}$	$9\overline{)63}$	$7\overline{)42}$	$9\overline{)18}$
$6\overline{)30}$	$9\overline{)54}$	$7\overline{)14}$	$6\overline{)42}$	$9\overline{)72}$	$7\overline{)56}$
$7\overline{)21}$	$6\overline{)6}$	$9\overline{)45}$	$8\overline{)72}$	$8\overline{)24}$	$6\overline{)36}$
$8\overline{)16}$	$9\overline{)27}$	$6\overline{)12}$	$7\overline{)49}$	$6\overline{)54}$	$8\overline{)48}$

Name _____

Teaching Resources

Teaching Resources

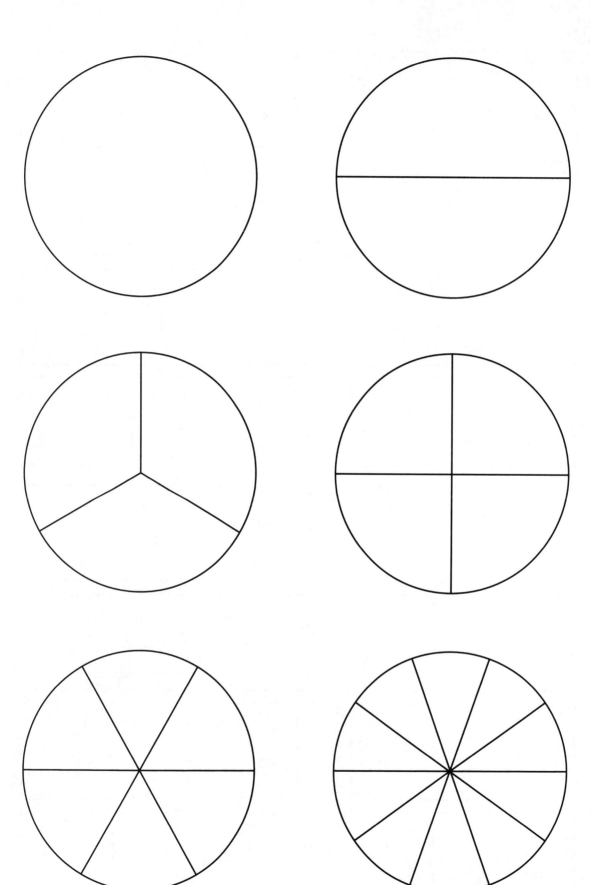

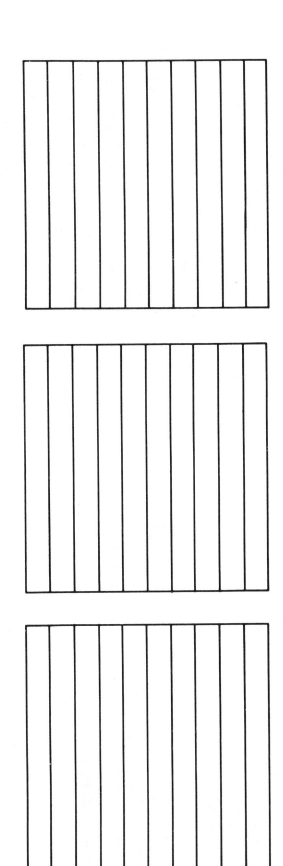

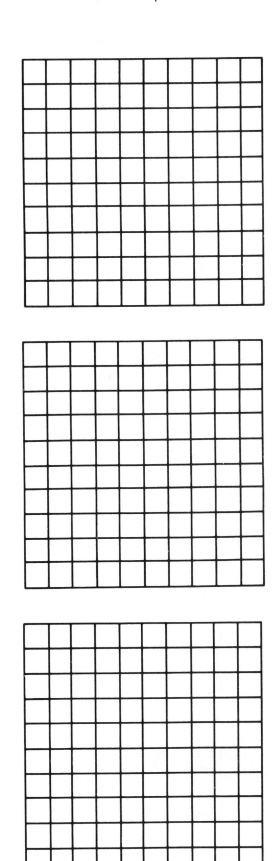

Teaching Resources

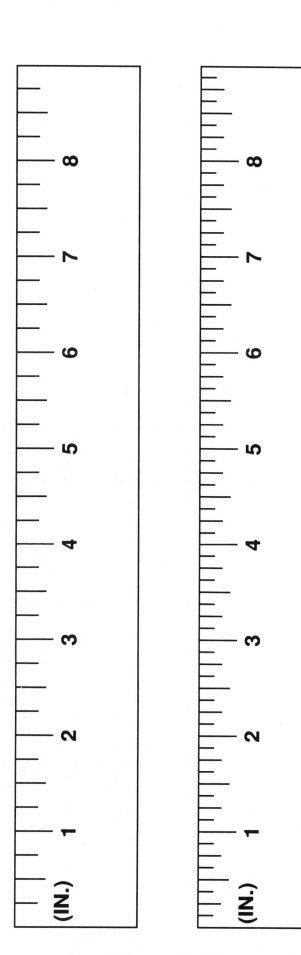

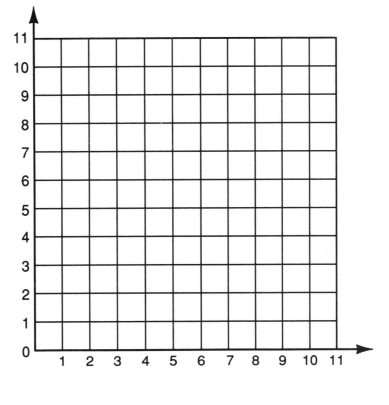

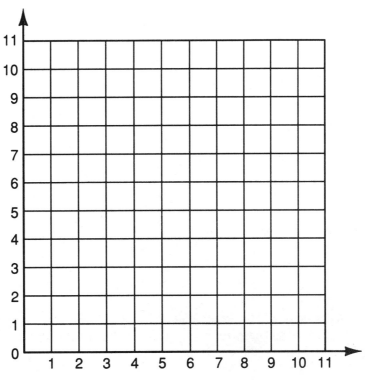

Teaching Resources

Help your child play this game to reinforce place value concepts for 4-digit numbers.

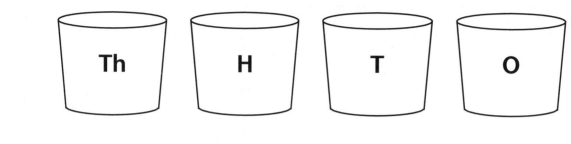

Round 1	_____	_____
Round 2	_____	_____
Round 3	_____	_____
Round 4	_____	_____
Round 5	_____	_____
Round 6	_____	_____
Round 7	_____	_____
Round 8	_____	_____
Round 9	_____	_____
Round 10	_____	_____

✂ -

Family Note:
- Gather 4 plastic containers, 9 small beans or buttons, and tape or string.
- Label the containers to match the picture above. Then set the containers in a row.
- Mark the floor about 3 feet from the containers using tape or the string.
- Take turns tossing 9 beans or buttons, one bean or button at a time, into the containers. If one lands outside, it is tossed again.
- When all 9 are in the containers, count the beans in each container. The number of beans represents the number of thousands, hundreds, tens, and ones. For example, if there are 3 beans in the thousands container, then there are 3 thousands. If there are no beans in the hundreds container, then there are 0 hundreds. Record the number.
- Whoever has the greater number wins the round. You may wish to set a rule that the number tossed each time must be different from the number previously tossed. This will eliminate the strategy of tossing all 9 beans in the thousands-container each time.
- The person to win the most rounds wins the game.

Use the number cube and the activity on this page to help your child practice adding 3-digit numbers.

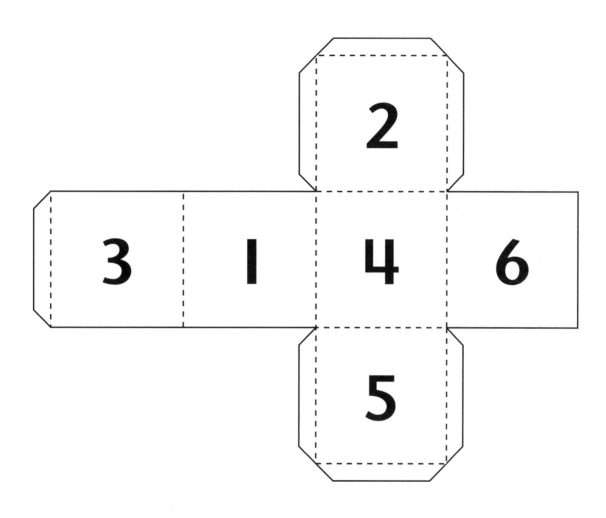

✂ -

Family Note:
- Cut out and fold the number cube pattern above.
- The goal of the activity is to arrange the digits in two 3-digit numbers so that, when they are added, the result is the greatest sum possible.
- Each player rolls the number cube 3 times.
- Players record the number rolled each time on a separate sheet.
- This sequence is repeated.
- Then players add their 2 numbers.
- The player with the greater sum wins each round.
- Play continues for 5 or more rounds.

Use the activity on this page to help your child practice subtracting 3-digit numbers.

Round 1	
Player _____	**Player** _____

Round 2	
Player _____	**Player** _____

Round 3	
Player _____	**Player** _____

Round 4	
Player _____	**Player** _____

✂ - ✂ - - -

Family Note:
- Use the number cube from Family Project, Unit 2.
- The goal of the activity is to arrange the digits in two 3-digit numbers so that, when the numbers are subtracted, the result is the least possible difference.
- Each player rolls the number cube 3 times.
- Players record the number rolled each time in the appropriate box above.
- This sequence is repeated. Remind your child to write the greater number first.
- Then players subtract their 2 numbers.
- The player with the lesser answer wins each round.
- Play continues for 4 or more rounds.

Use the flash cards on this page to help your child practice multiplication facts.

5 ×2	2 ×3	4 ×0	3 ×3	2 ×4
8 ×4	3 ×4	6 ×5	4 ×4	3 ×2
5 ×5	4 ×3	4 ×2	6 ×1	5 ×4
6 ×2	3 ×5	4 ×5	7 ×2	9 ×5
6 ×3	8 ×5	9 ×4	7 ×3	6 ×4

✂ –

Family Note:
- Cut out the cards above and those on p. 200 and place them in a stack with cards facing down.
- Divide the stack into two equal stacks.
- Give your child one stack and you take the other stack
- Each of you turns over the top card in your stack, and says the product.
- The player with the greater product takes both cards.
- If the products are equal, each player places another 2 cards face down and turns over a third card.
- The player that has the third card with the greater product takes all the cards.
- When a player's stack of cards is gone he or she may use cards from the "win" pile.
- Play continues until one player holds all the cards.

Family Projects

8 ×2	1 ×3	0 ×3	2 ×5	2 ×2
1 ×4	0 ×4	1 ×5	7 ×5	1 ×5
7 ×3	1 ×2	4 ×2	0 ×2	8 ×3
9 ×3	9 ×2			

Help your child apply what he or she has learned about multiplication and division fact families.

16	36	18
28	4	7
2	9	4

7	16	36	28	4	2	9

✂ ---

Family Note:
• Gather 2 sets of 5 buttons or beans for each player. Each set should be a different color.
• Play a game similar to tic-tac-toe. Players choose numbers and operations to produce 3 answers across or 3 answers down, using the numbers in the 2 tables above.
• Guide your child to choose two numbers from the smaller table. Help your child decide whether to multiply or divide the numbers.
• Check to see where the answer will be in the larger table.
• Help your child place a bean or button on his or her answer in the larger table.
• Take turns. Play continues until a player places 3 buttons or beans in a row, column, or diagonal.

Sample exercises: $7 \times 4 = 28$, $9 \times 4 = 36$, $16 \div 4 = 4$; $36 \div 4 = 9$, $36 \div 9 = 4$, $28 \div 4 = 7$, $28 \div 7 = 4$, $4 \times 4 = 16$, $2 \times 9 = 18$. .

Family Projects

Help your child use the grid and coordinates to practice plotting points.

1. (3,2)

2. (4,3)

3. (5,2)

4. (5,3)

5. (4,4)

6. (2,4)

7. (1,3)

8. (1,2)

9. (2,3)

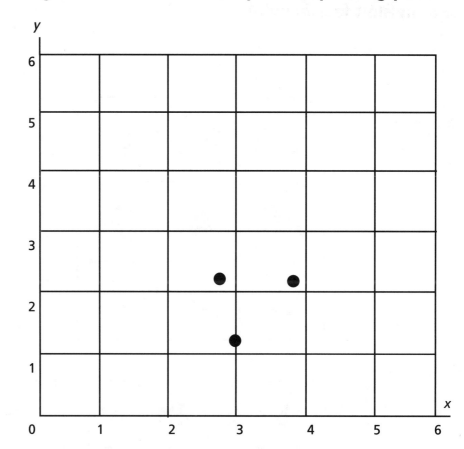

Family Note:
- Help your child plot the points described by the coordinate pairs above.
- Remind your child to go **across** to find the first number in the pair, and **up** for the second number in the pair.
- When your child has plotted all the points, ask him or her to predict what kind of animal is hidden. (Answer: a puppy with floppy ears)
- Help your child draw lines to connect the points. **Note:** *The points should be connected in order, starting with the point for exercise 1 and continuing to the point for exercise 9. When your child reaches the point for exercise 9, he or she should connect that point to the point for exercise 1.*
- Your child may wish to color and display the completed grid.

● **Help your child use what he or she knows about fractions as you play the game below.**

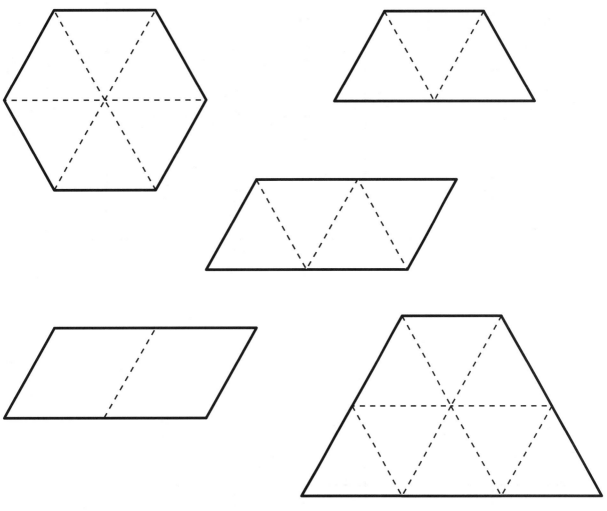

✂ -

Family Note:
- Gather scissors and crayons.
- Ask your child to color each figure with a different color crayon.
- Then help your child cut out the pieces.
- Next, place the pieces face down.
- Take turns picking 2 pieces.
- When a player has enough pieces to make a whole figure he or she scores a point.
- Play continues until all the pieces have been used.
- The player with the most "wholes" wins.
- Throughout the game, ask your child to name the fractional parts of their figures.
  EXAMPLE: Ask, "In the diamonds, what fraction of the whole is one part?" (one half and one fourth) "What fraction of the small trapezoid is 2 parts?" (two thirds) "What fraction of the hexagon is 5 parts?" (five sixths)

Family Projects

Use the flash cards on this page to help your child practice multiplication facts.

6 ×6	9 ×4	6 ×9	9 ×6	6 ×5
3 ×4	2 ×6	3 ×6	9 ×2	4 ×6
8 ×3	4 ×7	7 ×4	7 ×9	9 ×7
6 ×8	8 ×6	9 ×8	8 ×9	9 ×5
5 ×9	8 ×5	5 ×8	7 ×3	3 ×7

✂ --

Family Note:
- Help your child cut out the cards on this page.
- Arrange the cards facing down in rows and columns.
- Take turns turning over 2 cards each.
- If a player turns over cards with matching products, the player keeps both cards. The player must say the product before taking the cards.
- If there is no match, the cards are turned face down.
- Play continues until all the cards have been matched.
- The player with the most cards wins.

Use the example and the activity on this page and the number cube from Family Project Unit 2 to help your child practice multiplying a 1-digit and a 3-digit number.

Th	H	T	O
	6	2	2
×			3
1	8	6	6

Score Card

Round

1 738

2 + 1,866

  2,604

3

✂ --

Family Note:

- Help your child make a score card like the one above by folding a sheet of paper in half and labeling each half as shown.
- Use the number cube from Unit 2 Family Project or slips of paper numbered from 1 through 6.
- Each player rolls the number cube 4 times and records the digits on his or her scorecard. Remind your child to think about placing the greater digits in the greater place value positions.
  EXAMPLE: Suppose you roll 1, 3, 2, 7 — if you make 2 × 137, your score for that round is only 274. But if you make 3 × 721 your score is 2,163.
- Each player finds the product of the two numbers he or she made and records it in the scorecard.
- Scores are cumulative and added after each consecutive round.
- Play proceeds until a player reaches 10,000 or more.

Work with your child to find the area of different rectangles.

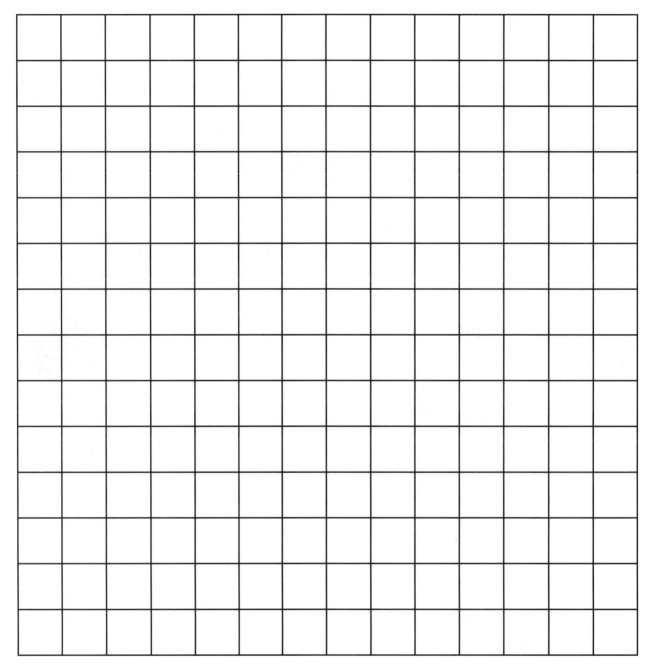

✂ ▬

Family Note:
• Work with your child to draw rectangles with the same perimeter, but with different areas. For example, see how many rectangles you can draw with a perimeter of 16 units. These are the possible dimensions:
4 units by 4 units, 3 units by 5 units, 2 units by 6 units, and 1 unit by 7 units.
Which has the greatest area?
• Try other perimeters such as 9 units, 25 units, and 36 units. What shape has the greatest area? (square)

Use the cards and activity on this page to help your child practice comparing decimals.

0.0	0.1	0.2	0.3	0.4
0.5	0.6	0.7	0.8	0.9
1.0	1.1	1.2	1.3	1.4
1.5	1.6	1.7	1.8	1.9
2.0	2.1	1.1	2.3	2.4
2.5	2.6	2.7	2.8	2.9

Family Note:
- Help your child cut out the decimal cards above.
- When the cards are ready, divide them evenly. Place the stacks face down in front of each player.
- Each player shows the top card in his or her stack.
- Help your child compare the decimals, first by comparing digits in the ones place, then comparing digits in the tenths place. If your child is having difficulty comparing digit for digit, align the numbers as shown below:

    2.3
    2.4 ← greater number
- The player with the greater number wins both cards.
- The player with more cards at the end wins.
- Play may continue until one player retains all the cards.

Family Projects

Answer Keys

NOTES

Answer Key
Beginning of the Year Inventory

1. 7
2. 10
3. 12
4. 5
5. 8
6. 6
7. 4
8. 9
9. 8
10. 60
11. 60
12. 24
13. 7
14. 12
15. 365
16. 5; 4 + 5 = 9; 9 − 4 = 5; 9 − 5 = 4
17. 6; 6 + 0 = 6; 6 − 0 = 6; 6 − 6 = 0
18. 7 + 9 = 16; 9 + 7 = 16; 16 − 9 = 7; 16 − 7 = 9
19. 7 + 6 = 13; 6 + 7 = 13; 13 − 7 = 6; 13 − 6 = 7
20. triangle
21. rectangle
22. sphere
23. cube
24. cylinder and cone
25. pyramid and prism
26. $.48
27. 38
28. 213
29. 401
30. 52
31. 386
32. 902
33. 93
34. 130
35. 408
36. 612
37. 504
38. >

39. <
40. =
41. <
42. <
43. >
44. seventy-five
45. two hundred two
46. 70
47. 20
48. 50
49. 100
50. 400
51. 600
52. 1,000
53. 2,000
54. 4,000
55. 6
56. more than
57. less than
58. about equal
59. 5
60. 4, 6, 8, 10, 12, 14, 16, 18, 20
61. 6, 9, 12, 15, 18, 21, 24, 27, 30
62. 10, 15, 20, 25, 30, 35, 40, 45, 50
63. 20, 30, 40, 50, 60, 70, 80, 90, 100
64. 14
65. 13
66. 14
67. 47
68. 79
69. 67
70. 99
71. 37
72. 92
73. 56
74. 132
75. 75
76. 36
77. 52
78. 77
79. 20
80. 59

81. 12
82. 27
83. 25
84. 53
85. 39
86. 54
87. 24
88. 53
89. 9:00
90. 7:15
91. 2:30
92. 7:30
93. $\frac{1}{6}$
94. $\frac{2}{3}$
95. $\frac{3}{4}$
96. $6.49
97. $5.48
98. $4.32
99. $1.61
100. 8; 8; 8; 8
101. 6; 2; 12; 0; 10
102. 20; 10; 5; 15; 0
103. 30; 0; 50; 10; 20
104. 5
105. never; sometimes; always; sometimes
106. 12 apples
107. 36
108. hot dog and banana
109. 14 − 8 = 6 pictures
110. 12 model cars
111. 7 pages
112. 32 people
113. red roses
114. 5 people
115. 5 people
116. 3 people
117. brown
118. green
119. 10

Answer Key • Pretests and Posttests

Unit 1 Pretest

1. 317
2. 2,106
3. 600 + 40 + 8
4. 7, 1
5. 2,513
6. 4,000 + 900 + 20 + 5
7. $.54
8. $1.32
9. 69, 70, 71, 72
10. 450, 460, 470, 480
11. 5,300; 5,400; 5,500; 5,600
12. >, =, <
13. <, >, >
14. <, <, <
15. 15 minutes after 4 or 4:15
16. 20 minutes after 9 or 9:20
17. half past 11 or 11:30
18. Thursday
19. third
20. 2nd, 4th, 6th
21. Possible answer: every 3 days
22. 7:45 P.M.

Unit 1 Posttest

1. 209
2. 1,355
3. 200 + 90 + 7
4. 3, 6
5. 5,279
6. 1,000 + 800 + 60 + 2
7. $.61
8. $1.40
9. 90, 91, 92, 93
10. 360, 370, 380, 390
11. 3,500; 3,600; 3,700; 3,800
12. <, >, <
13. >, >, >
14. =, <, <
15. 15 minutes before 2 or 1:45
16. 50 minutes after 4 or 4:50
17. half past 2 or 2:30
18. Tuesday
19. fourth
20. 2nd, 3rd, 5th
21. Possible answer: every 6 days
22. 11:45 P.M.

Unit 2 Pretest

1. 447
2. 833
3. $3.94
4. 441
5. 6,013
6. $7.63
7. 815
8. 8,594
9. $4.27
10. 626
11. $8.61
12. 4,948
13. 50
14. 2,000
15. 320
16. 800
17. 1,600
18. 6,240
19. 70 + 60 = 130
20. 130 + 20 = 150
21. 90 + 30 = 120
22. 86; Possible answer: conjecture and verify
23. 44 cards; 35 cards

Unit 2 Posttest

1. 294
2. 633
3. $4.39
4. 543
5. 7,983
6. $8.47
7. 747
8. 7,928
9. $5.18
10. 447
11. $9.34
12. 7,048
13. 30
14. 1,000
15. 720
16. 900
17. 3,700
18. 2,190
19. 90 + 20 = 110
20. 110 + 20 = 130
21. 90 + 40 = 130
22. 39; Possible answer: conjecture and verify
23. 34 models; 25 models

Unit 3 Pretest

1. $2.78
2. 558
3. $2.36
4. $7.57

(Unit 3 Pretest continued)

5. 623
6. $5.76
7. 281
8. 328
9. $2.82
10. $2.14
11. 259
12. 248
13. 537
14. 232
15. 1,440
16. $6.86
17. 1,251
18. 373
19. 2,201
20. 2,062
21. 70 − 20 = 50
22. 100 − 20 = 80
23. 70 − 40 = 30
24. a nickel, a dime, a quarter; $.40
25. 3 more rows

Unit 3 Posttest

1. $2.73
2. 518
3. $3.42
4. $2.26
5. 405
6. $3.84
7. 272
8. 511
9. $3.16
10. $10.02
11. 269
12. 433
13. 735
14. 335
15. 1,682
16. $3.57
17. 2,014
18. 381
19. 2,813
20. 4,718
21. 50 − 30 = 20
22. 80 − 50 = 30
23. 50 − 10 = 40
24. 2 pennies, a nickel, a dime; $.17
25. 2 more rows

Unit 4 Pretest

1. 3
2. 24
3. 8
4. 0
5. 15

(Unit 4 Pretest continued)

6. 16
7. 9
8. 30
9. 32
10. 21
11. 5
12. 40
13. 3; 15; 24; 6; 12; 18; 30
14. 0; 4; 20; 8; 16; 24; 40
15. 0; 5; 25; 40; 20; 30; 50
16. 28; 4 × 7 = 28
17. 27; 3 × 9 = 27
18. 6 × 3 = 18; 2 × 9 = 18
19. Lee; 14 books
20. 32 books; Possible answer: Skip-count by 2s.

Unit 4 Posttest

1. 9
2. 10
3. 28
4. 0
5. 24
6. 25
7. 12
8. 40
9. 21
10. 20
11. 6
12. 24
13. 3; 12; 18; 15; 27; 9; 30
14. 0; 4; 16; 24; 20; 12; 40
15. 0; 5; 20; 30; 25; 15; 50
16. 18; 3 × 6 = 18
17. 40; 5 × 8 = 40
18. 4 × 5 = 20; 2 × 10 = 20
19. burgers; 14 people
20. 36 people; Possible answer: Skip-count by 2s.

Unit 5 Pretest

1. 3
2. 5
3. 5
4. 3
5. 5
6. 5
7. 3
8. 3
9. 3
10. 5
11. 4
12. 5
13. 4, 4, 12
14. 6, 6, 18
15. 5, 5, 20
16. 6, 6, 12

Answer Key • Pretests and Posttests

(Unit 5 Pretest continued)

17. $6 \times 3 = 18$; $3 \times 6 = 18$; $18 \div 6 = 3$; $18 \div 3 = 6$
18. $3
19. $2
20. 8 cans
21. 4 pencils

Unit 5 Posttest

1. 2
2. 4
3. 6
4. 3
5. 2
6. 8
7. 7
8. 3
9. 2
10. 3
11. 7
12. 5
13. 5, 5, 15
14. 3, 3, 12
15. 7, 7, 28
16. 9, 9, 18
17. $6 \times 4 = 24$; $4 \times 6 = 24$; $24 \div 6 = 4$; $24 \div 4 = 6$
18. $5
19. $8
20. 4 stamps
21. 7 beads

Unit 6 Pretest

1. rectangle
2. pentagon
3. square
4. hexagon
5. triangle
6. octagon
7. less than
8. right angle
9. greater than
10. false
11. true
12. true
13. false
14. false
15. true
16. Triangles and pentagons are congruent.
17. equilateral
18. scalene
19. isosceles
20. right
21. cylinder
22. cube

(Unit 6 Pretest continued)

23. sphere; Cylinder and sphere will roll.
24. certain
25. likely
26. unlikely
27. Dog: 14; Cat: 8; Fish: 4; Dog
28. 3 ft, 4 ft, 7 ft, 9 ft

Unit 6 Posttest

1. square
2. octagon
3. hexagon
4. triangle
5. rectangle
6. pentagon
7. greater than
8. right angle
9. less
10. false
11. true
12. false
13. true
14. true
15. true
16. Triangles are not congruent.
17. scalene
18. right
19. equilateral
20. isosceles
21. pyramid
22. rectangular prism
23. cone; Cone will roll.
24. impossible
25. likely
26. certain
27. Blue: 9; Green: 6; Red: 12; Red
28. 4, 7, 8

Unit 7 Pretest

1. $\frac{1}{2}$
2. $\frac{1}{4}$
3. $\frac{3}{8}$
4. $\frac{1}{3}$
5. $\frac{2}{3}$
6. $\frac{1}{5}$
7. $\frac{1}{4}$
8. $\frac{4}{6}$
9. <

(Unit 7 Pretest continued)

10. >
11. =
12. $\frac{5}{6}, \frac{3}{6}, \frac{1}{6}$
13. $\frac{7}{7}, \frac{4}{7}, \frac{2}{7}$
14. 2
15. 6
16. 2
17. 4
18. 2
19. 3
20. 1
21. 0
22. $4\frac{1}{8}$
23. $1\frac{2}{3}$
24. Don't know, the cost of the carton of milk is missing.
25. Yes; $\frac{3}{4} + 1 + \frac{1}{4} = 2$ cups.
26. $\frac{2}{8}$; subtraction; needed to find the difference
27. $\frac{5}{10}$ are blue and yellow.

Unit 7 Posttest

1. $\frac{1}{5}$
2. $\frac{2}{8}$
3. $\frac{1}{4}$
4. $\frac{1}{6}$
5. $\frac{1}{5}$
6. $\frac{3}{6}$
7. $\frac{1}{3}$
8. $\frac{1}{8}$
9. =
10. >
11. <
12. $\frac{7}{8}, \frac{5}{8}, \frac{2}{8}$
13. $\frac{4}{4}, \frac{3}{4}, \frac{1}{4}$
14. 2
15. 6
16. 4
17. 3
18. 2
19. 4
20. $\frac{1}{2}$
21. 1

(Unit 7 Posttest continued)

22. $4\frac{3}{4}$
23. $1\frac{5}{6}$
24. Don't know, the amount of money he has is missing.
25. No; $\frac{1}{3} + 1 + \frac{2}{3} = 2$ cups.
26. $\frac{2}{10}$; subtraction; needed to find the difference
27. $\frac{7}{8}$ are apples and bananas.

Unit 8 Pretest

1. 48
2. 9
3. 49
4. 63
5. 40
6. 54
7. 27
8. 56
9. 72
10. 4
11. 6
12. 8
13. 3
14. 5
15. 8
16. 7
17. 4
18. 8
19. 7 R1
20. 7 R3
21. 7 R5
22. 6, 7, 4, 46
23. $8 \times 5 = 40$ miles
24. 9 necklaces

Unit 8 Posttest

1. 42
2. 45
3. 0
4. 72
5. 32
6. 48
7. 21
8. 54
9. 81
10. 7
11. 7
12. 7
13. 3
14. 6
15. 6
16. 6
17. 5
18. 6

Answer Key • Pretests and Posttests

(Unit 8 Posttest continued)
19. 7 R3
20. 5 R3
21. 8 R2
22. 6, 9, 2, 56
23. $7 \times 6 = 42$ miles
24. 8 pages

Unit 9 Pretest

1. 68
2. 69
3. 77
4. 1,204
5. 495
6. 424
7. 192
8. 2,520
9. 666
10. 430
11. 159
12. 2,864
13. 652
14. 2,552
15. 1,144
16. 6,876
17. $7.56
18. $18.72
19. $8.04
20. $83.92
21. 12 R2
22. 143
23. 13 days
24. 7 purple beads

Unit 9 Posttest

1. 86
2. 66
3. 99
4. 812
5. 684
6. 496
7. 258
8. 1,545
9. 498
10. 395
11. 177
12. 3,468
13. 628
14. 3,424
15. 1,436
16. 5,805
17. $7.80
18. $18.32
19. $8.52
20. $85.04

(Unit 9 Posttest continued)
21. 13 R3
22. 169
23. 16 days
24. 8 blue marbles

Unit 10 Pretest

1. 6
2. 2
3. 12
4. 3 oz
5. 3 ft
6. 10 kg
7. 98°C
8. 89°F
9. 2
10. 4
11. 2
12. 2
13. 12
14. 3
15. 4
16. 16
17. 24
18. 15
19. 21
20. 9
21. 6
22. 15
23. 4
24. 10
25. 4
26. 40°F

Unit 10 Posttest

1. 7
2. 10
3. 3
4. 5 lb
5. 8 ft
6. 5 kg
7. 18°C
8. 68°F
9. 3
10. 2
11. 2
12. 16
13. 3
14. 12
15. 4
16. 36
17. 32
18. 18
19. 21
20. 25

(Unit 10 Posttest continued)
21. 12
22. 18
23. 9
24. 16
25. 8
26. 50°F

Unit 11 Pretest

1. 0.6
2. 0.24
3. 1.2
4. 0.02
5. 0.53
6. 0.4
7. 22.0
8. 4.4
9. 9.6
10. 18.1
11. $21.52
12. $21.84
13. $1.06
14. $2.36
15. $0.2; \frac{2}{10}$
16. $\frac{1}{2}; 0.50$
17. Yes; She does have enough money because $4 \times \$13 < \$60$.
18. $4.88

Unit 11 Posttest

1. 0.8
2. 0.63
3. 1.4
4. 0.05
5. 0.82
6. 0.9
7. 21.2
8. 4.9
9. 8.5
10. 13.4
11. $13.04
12. $45.60
13. $1.03
14. $3.45
15. $0.6; \frac{6}{10}$
16. $0.25; \frac{25}{100}$
17. No; He does not have enough money because $4 \times \$14 > \$50$.
18. $6.45

Answer Key • Midyear Test

1. B	**23.** D
2. H	**24.** G
3. C	**25.** D
4. J	**26.** G
5. C	**27.** D
6. J	**28.** J
7. B	**29.** D
8. H	**30.** H
9. C	**31.** A
10. F	**32.** J
11. A	**33.** C
12. G	**34.** H
13. D	**35.** D
14. H	**36.** K
15. D	**37.** A
16. H	**38.** J
17. B	**39.** C
18. G	**40.** J
19. D	**41.** C
20. J	**42.** G
21. C	**43.** B
22. J	**44.** H

Answer Keys

Answer Key • Final Test

1.	C	32.	H
2.	G	33.	B
3.	B	34.	H
4.	H	35.	D
5.	C	36.	H
6.	J	37.	B
7.	A	38.	H
8.	J	39.	B
9.	C	40.	G
10.	G	41.	D
11.	A	42.	J
12.	J	43.	C
13.	C	44.	K
14.	J	45.	D
15.	B	46.	K
16.	J	47.	A
17.	D	48.	F
18.	G	49.	D
19.	C	50.	G
20.	H	51.	B
21.	B	52.	G
22.	J	53.	C
23.	A	54.	J
24.	G	55.	C
25.	C	56.	J
26.	F	57.	B
27.	B	58.	J
28.	H	59.	A
29.	C	60.	H
30.	F	61.	B
31.	D	62.	H

Answer Key • Reteach Worksheets

Reteach 1, page 59
1. b
2. d
3. c
4. a
5. 4:00

Reteach 2, page 60
1. >
2. >
3. <
4. 78, 87, 88, 107
5. 234, 423, 432, 443
6. 456, 554, 654, 655
7. 3,559; 3,589; 3,598; 3,895

Reteach 3, page 61
1. 1,208
2. 3,005
3. 6,852
4. 4,537
5. 7,210
6. 5,979
7. 3,062
8. 4,508
9. 2,173
10. 6,624

Reteach 4, page 62
1. 100,000 + 80,000 + 7,000 + 20 + 9
2. 60,000 + 2,000 + 100 + 7
3. 60,000 + 7,000 + 400 + 20 + 1
4. 900,000
5. 50,000
6. 8,000
7. 0
8. 70
9. 2

Reteach 5, page 63
1. >
2. >
3. >
4. <
5. >
6. <

Reteach 6, page 64
1. 1; $3.41
2. 1; 2; $2.12
3. 1; 6; 5; $1.65
4. 4; 0; 4; $4.04

Reteach 7, page 65
1. 10
2. quarter; 25
3. quarter; 25
4. half-dollar; 50
5. half-dollar; 50
6. nickel; 5

Reteach 8, page 66
1. $2.35
2. $1.28
3. $1.45
4. $2.50
5. $.95
6. $1.15

Reteach 9, page 67
1. 5¢
2. 6¢
3. 1 penny, 1 quarter; 26¢
4. 1 dime; 10¢
5. 3 pennies; 3¢
6. 1 penny, 1 dime; 11¢

Reteach 10, page 68
1. Friday
2. Thursday
3. Monday
4. Saturday
5. November 3rd
6. November 8th
7. b
8. Thursday

Reteach 11, page 69
1. 5:10
2. 8; 8:05
3. 10:45

Reteach 12, page 70
1. 10:08
2. 9; 9:23
3. 6:42
4. 4:00; 3:53

Reteach 13, page 71
1. 1:30 P.M.
2. 9:00 A.M.
3. 4:15 P.M.
4. 10:30 A.M.
5. 7:00 A.M.
6. 5:30 P.M.

Reteach 14, page 72
1. 30; 20; 20; 30
2. 50; 60; 60; 50
3. 400; 500; 500; 400
4. 600; 700; 600; 600

Reteach 15, page 73
1. 3,000; 5,000; 8,000
2. 7,000; 5,000; 2,000; 5,000
3. 5,000; 2,000; 8,000; 4,000

Reteach 16, page 74
1. 80
2. 110
3. 170
4. 30; 40; 70
5. 60; 60; 120
6. 40; 90; 130
7. 10; 60; 70
8. 70; 90; 160
9. 80; 40; 120
10. 30; 40; 70
11. 10; 60; 70
12. 30; 90; 120
13. 30; 10; 40
14. 50; 20; 70
15. 50; 20; 70

Reteach 17, page 75
1. $6.13
2. $6.52
3. $3.93
4. $6.23
5. $2.76
6. $9.02
7. $6.68
8. $4.44
9. $8.41

Reteach 18, page 76
1. 281
2. 213
3. 352
4. 248
5. 126
6. 84
7. 317
8. 315

Reteach 19, page 77
1. $4.84
2. $1.67
3. $1.37
4. $4.11
5. $2.51

(Reteach 19 continued)
6. $3.22
7. $2.76
8. $2.34
9. $1.83
10. $2.15
11. $1.28
12. $4.54

Reteach 20, page 78
1. 20
2. 50
3. 50
4. 90; 40; 50
5. 70; 30; 40
6. 90; 30; 60
7. 50; 40; 10
8. 90; 30; 60
9. 80; 40; 40
10. 80; 50; 30
11. 90; 60; 30
12. 70; 20; 50
13. 30; 10; 20
14. 70; 30; 40
15. 70; 20; 50

Reteach 21, page 79
1. 2, 4, 6, 8, 10, 12; 6; 12
2. 3, 6, 9, 12, 15, 18, 21; 7; 21
3. 4, 8, 12, 16, 20, 24, 28; 7; 28
4. 5, 10, 15, 20, 25, 30, 35; 7; 35
5. 10, 20, 30, 40; 4; 40

Reteach 22, page 80
1. 4; 4; 2; 8;
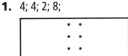
2. 3; 3; 4; 12;

3. 5; 15; 5; 3; 5; 3; 15;
4. 5; 10; 5; 2; 5; 2; 10;

Answer Keys

Answer Key • Reteach Worksheets

Reteach 23, page 81

1. 6; 6
2. 8; 8
3. 12; 6, 12
4. 4; 2, 4
5. 14; 7, 2, 14
6. 18; 9, 2, 18
7. 16; 8, 2, 16

Reteach 24, page 82

1. 12
2. 6
3. 16
4. 14
5. 4
6. 10
7. 2
8. 0
9. 14
10. 8
11. 16
12. 10
13. 0
14. 6
15. 2
16. 12
17. 16
18. 10
19. 18
20. 14

Reteach 25, page 83

1. 8; 8
2. 10; 10
3. 16; 16
4. 2; 2
5. 12; 6, 12
6. 18; 9, 18
7. 0; 2, 0, 0
8. 14; 2, 7, 14
9. 8; 8
10. 12; 2, 12
11. 10, 10; 2, 10

Reteach 26, page 84

1. 3
2. 2
3. 4
4. 5
5. 8
6. 9
7. 0
8. 0
9. 0
10. 0
11. 0
12. 0

(Reteach 26 continued)

13. 2
14. 8
15. 0
16. 9
17. 1
18. 1
19. 8
20. 0
21. 7
22. 0
23. 0
24. 0
25. 5
26. 0

Reteach 27, page 85

1. 10
2. 25
3. 15
4. 5
5. 30
6. 40
7. 35
8. 20
9. 45
10. 0

Reteach 28, page 86

1. 4; 4; 16; 16
2. 5; 4; 20; 4, 20
3. 12
4. 8
5. 32
6. 20
7. 36
8. 24
9. 0
10. 16
11. 12
12. 4
13. 8

Reteach 29, page 87

1. 80; 60; 70; 80
2. 50; 30; 40; 50
3. 30; 10; 20; 30
4. 40; 10; 20; 30; 40
5. 70
6. 90
7. 30
8. 40
9. 90
10. 50
11. 0
12. 20
13. 10

(Reteach 29 continued)

14. 60
15. 80

Reteach 30, page 88

1. 3, 6; 6, 3, 3; 3, 3, 0; 4
2. 15; 5
3. 18; 6
4. 27; 9
5. 21; 7

Reteach 31, page 89

1. 5
2. 2
3. 3; 3
4. 7; 7
5. 8; 8
6. 4; 4
7. 1; 1
8. 9; 9

Reteach 32, page 90

1. 6
2. 10
3. 6, 12
4. 1; 1, 2
5. 8; 8, 2, 16
6. 7; 7, 2, 14
7. 9; 9, 2, 18
8. 2; 2, 2, 4

Reteach 33, page 91

1. 14; 2; 14
2. 4; 8; 2; 8
3. 2; 12; 12
4. 8; 2; 16; 16
5. 1; 2; 2; 2
6. 3; 2; 3, 6; 2, 3, 6
7. 9; 2; 9, 18; 2, 9, 18
8. 4; 4, 2; 4, 8; 2, 4, 8

Reteach 34, page 92

1. 1
2. 0
3. 5
4. 1
5. 8
6. 0
7. 6
8. 1
9. 0
10. 9
11. 1
12. 1

Reteach 35, page 93

1. 4
2. 8
3. 3
4. 1
5. 7
6. 8
7. 9
8. 1
9. 4
10. 2
11. 3
12. 6
13. 5
14. 7

Reteach 36, page 94

1. 35; 7; 35, 5
2. 10; 2; 5, 2, 10; 10, 2, 5
3. 45; 5, 9, 45; 9; 45, 9, 5
4. 30; 6, 5, 30; 30, 6, 5; 30, 5, 6
5. 5; 5, 1, 5; 5, 5, 1; 5, 1, 5
6. 15; 3, 5, 15; 15, 3, 5; 15, 5, 3
7. 40; 5, 8, 40; 40, 5, 8; 40, 8, 5
8. 25; 25, 5, 5

Reteach 37, page 95

1. 12; 4; 12; 3
2. 20; 5; 4, 5, 20; 20, 5, 4
3. 36; 4, 9, 36; 9; 36, 9, 4
4. 28; 7, 4, 28; 28, 7, 4; 28, 4, 7
5. 4; 4, 1, 4; 4, 4, 1; 4, 1, 4
6. 8; 2, 4, 8; 8, 2, 4; 8, 4, 2
7. 32; 4, 8, 32; 32, 4, 8; 32, 8, 4
8. 16; 16, 4, 4

Reteach 38, page 96

1. 15; 5; 15; 15, 5, 3
2. 12; 3; 4, 3, 12; 12, 3, 4
3. 18; 3, 6, 18; 6; 18, 6, 3
4. 6; 2, 3, 6; 6, 2, 3; 6, 3, 2
5. 3; 1, 3, 3; 3, 1, 3; 3, 3, 1
6. 27; 3, 9, 27; 27, 3, 9; 27, 9, 3
7. 24; 8, 3, 24; 24, 8, 3; 24, 3, 8
8. 9; 9, 3, 3

Answer Key • Reteach Worksheets

Reteach 39, page 97

1. 5
2. 6¢
3. 5; 5¢
4. 4; 4¢
5. 24 ÷ 8 = 3; 3¢
6. 8 ÷ 4 = 2; 2¢
7. 18 ÷ 3 = 6; 6¢
8. 32 ÷ 8 = 4; 4¢
9. 40 ÷ 5 = 8; 8¢
10. 18 ÷ 2 = 9; 9¢
11. 32 ÷ 4 = 8; 8¢
12. 21 ÷ 3 = 7; 7¢

Reteach 40, page 98

1. 0
2. 3
3. 4; 4
4. 4; 4
5. sphere
6. cube
7. cylinder
8. cone

Reteach 41, page 99

1. sometimes
2. always
3. sometimes
4. sometimes
5. always
6. never
7. sometimes
8. sometimes

Reteach 42, page 100

1. 3; 3
2. 5; 5
3. 6; 6
4. 8; 8
5. rectangle
6. octagon
7. triangle
8. hexagon
9. pentagon
10. square

Reteach 43, page 101

1. right angle
2. less than a right angle
3. right angle
4. less than a right angle
5. greater than a right angle
6. right angle

Reteach 44, page 102

1. not parallel
2. not parallel
3. parallel
4. parallel
5. 2
6. 0
7. 2
8. 2

Reteach 45, page 103

1. equilateral
2. isosceles
3. scalene
4. scalene
5. equilateral
6. scalene
7. scalene
8. scalene, circled
9. scalene
10. scalene
11. scalene, circled
12. 2

Reteach 46, page 104

1. squares are congruent
2. larger circles are congruent
3. right triangles are congruent
4. rectangles are congruent
5. Yes.
6. No.
7. Yes.

Reteach 47, page 105

1. cone
2. pyramid
3. cylinder
4. cone
5. sphere
6. cube
7. rectangular prism
8. cylinder

Reteach 48, page 106

1. (0, 2)
2. (4, 3)
3. (5, 5)
4. (6, 1)
5. C
6. F
7. B
8. K
9. L
10. E
11. I

(Reteach 48 continued)

12. G
13. (2, 2); (3, 6); (1, 4)
14. (4, 3); (4, 5); (6, 3); (6, 5)
15. (2, 0); (6, 0); (2, 1); (6, 1)

Reteach 49, page 107

1. Yellow: 4
2. Blue: 10
3. Green: 8
4. 5
5. 1
6. 4
7. 2
8. blue
9. orange
10. 36

Reteach 50, page 108

1. certain
2. unlikely
3. impossible
4. likely
5. likely
6. certain
7. unlikely
8. impossible

Reteach 51, page 109

1. 0
2. 1
3. 4
4. 5
5. 2
6. 71°
7. 65°, 74°
8. 18 days
9. Yes.
10. No.
11. Yes.

Reteach 52, page 110

1. No.
2. No.
3. Yes.
4. Yes.
5. $\frac{1}{3}$
6. $\frac{2}{4}$
7. $\frac{1}{3}$
8. $\frac{2}{4}$

Reteach 53, page 111

1. <
2. >
3. >
4. <
5. >
6. <
7. $\frac{3}{4}, \frac{2}{4}, \frac{1}{4}$
8. $\frac{4}{5}, \frac{3}{5}, \frac{2}{5}$
9. $\frac{5}{6}, \frac{2}{6}, \frac{1}{6}$

Reteach 54, page 112

1. 2
2. 2
3. 3
4. 8
5. 6
6. 10
7. 4
8. 10
9. 2
10. 2
11. 8
12. 5

Reteach 55, page 113

1. 3
2. 2
3. 5
4. 2
5. 4
6. 2
7. 4
8. 3
9. 8

Reteach 56, page 114

1. 2; 2
2. 2
3. 3; 3
4. 6
5. 4; 4
6. 4; 4
7. 8; 8
8. 5; 5
9. 1; 1

Answer Key • Reteach Worksheets

Reteach 57, page 115

1. $1\frac{1}{2}$
2. $2\frac{2}{6}$
3. $1\frac{5}{8}$
4. $2\frac{3}{4}$
5. $2\frac{1}{8}$
6. $3\frac{1}{4}$
7. $1\frac{2}{3}$
8. $1\frac{1}{6}$
9. $1\frac{1}{4}$
10. $1\frac{5}{8}$
11. $2\frac{1}{6}$
12. $1\frac{2}{3}$
13. $2\frac{3}{4}$
14. $3\frac{1}{2}$

Reteach 58, page 116

1. 0; 0; 0; 0; 0; 0; 0; 0; 0; 0
2. 0; 1; 2; 3; 4; 5; 6; 7; 8; 9
3. 0; 2; 4; 6; 8; 10; 12; 14; 16; 18
4. 0; 3; 6; 9; 12; 15; 18; 21; 24; 27
5. 0; 4; 8; 12; 16; 20; 24; 28; 32; 36
6. 0; 5; 10; 15; 20; 25; 30; 35; 40; 45

Reteach 59, page 117

1. 16; 2
2. 15; 5, 3, 15; 3; 15, 3, 5
3. 36; 4, 9, 36; 9; 36, 9, 4
4. 21; 3, 7, 21; 21, 7, 3; 21, 3, 7
5. 40; 5, 8, 40; 40, 8, 5; 40, 5, 8
6. 6; 2, 3, 6; 6, 3, 2; 6, 2, 3
7. 5; 5, 1, 5; 5, 5, 1; 5, 1, 5
8. 28; 4, 7, 28; 28; 7, 4; 28, 4, 7
9. 24; 3, 8, 24; 24, 8, 3; 24, 3, 8
10. 35; 5, 7, 35; 35, 5, 7; 35, 7, 5

(Reteach 59 continued)

11. 24; 4, 6, 24; 24, 6, 4; 24, 4, 6
12. 18; 2, 9, 18; 18, 9, 2; 18, 2, 9

Reteach 60, page 118

1. 42
2. 54
3. 36
4. 24
5. 36
6. 24
7. 12
8. 48
9. 18
10. 6
11. 42
12. 54
13. 30
14. 4
15. 8
16. 7
17. 2
18. 5
19. 3
20. 6
21. 1
22. 9

Reteach 61, page 119

1. 56
2. 49
3. 35
4. 42
5. 28
6. 21
7. 0
8. 49
9. 56
10. 14
11. 42
12. 63
13. 35
14. 3
15. 7
16. 6
17. 9
18. 8
19. 5
20. 2
21. 1
22. 4

Reteach 62, page 120

1. 72
2. 48
3. 24
4. 64
5. 40
6. 32
7. 8
8. 72
9. 24
10. 16
11. 56
12. 48
13. 64
14. 3
15. 1
16. 5
17. 6
18. 7
19. 4
20. 2
21. 9
22. 8

Reteach 63, page 121

1. 5 R1
2. 5 R2
3. 4 R3
4. 7 R1
5. 2 R2
6. 4 R2
7. 2 R2
8. 4 R1
9. 2 R2

Reteach 64, page 122

1. $(5 \times 4) + 1 = 20 + 1 = 21$
2. $3 \times 5 + 2 = 15 + 2 = 17$
3. 4 R2; $4 \times 3 + 2 = 14$
4. 3 R4; $3 \times 7 + 4 = 25$
5. 4 R4; $4 \times 5 + 4 = 24$
6. 5 R2; $5 \times 6 + 2 = 32$

Reteach 65, page 123

1. 1 apple
2. 5 boxes
3. 6 vases
4. 7 groups

Reteach 66, page 124

1. 900
2. 3,200
3. 1,800
4. 2,100
5. 3,000

(Reteach 66 continued)

6. 1,200
7. 800
8. 3,500
9. 2,400
10. 1,200
11. 2,800
12. 2,500
13. 400
14. 600
15. 1,200
16. 2,700
17. 2,700
18. 2,000
19. 1,200
20. 1,600
21. 600
22. 4,800
23. 1,600
24. 1,600
25. 1,000
26. 1,800
27. 2,800
28. 3,200
29. 3,600
30. 1,500

Reteach 67, page 125

1. 46
2. 93
3. 84
4. 28
5. 58
6. 48
7. 68
8. 69
9. 39
10. 66
11. 80
12. 39

Reteach 68, page 126

1. 92
2. 75
3. 68
4. 81
5. 92
6. 96
7. 96
8. 87
9. 70
10. 140
11. 138
12. 135
13. 108
14. 134

Answer Key • Reteach Worksheets

Reteach 69, page 127

1. 917
2. 724
3. 759
4. 740
5. 506
6. 968
7. 762
8. 846
9. 608
10. 849
11. 783
12. 768

Reteach 70, page 128

1. 2,440
2. 1,380
3. 1,035
4. 1,527
5. 3,010
6. 2,070
7. 1,025
8. 2,454
9. 2,100
10. 3,540
11. 3,012
12. 1,950
13. 872
14. 1,530
15. 4,812
16. 4,214
17. 3,616
18. 2,400
19. 1,580
20. 1,540

Reteach 71, page 129

1.–8. Answers will vary.
Check students' work.

Reteach 72, page 130

1. a
2. a
3. b
4. a
5. b
6. b
7. b
8. a
9. a
10. b
11. b
12. a

Reteach 73, page 131

1. a
2. a
3. b
4. a
5. a
6. b
7. b
8. a
9. a
10. b
11. b
12. b

Reteach 74, page 132

1. 2 in.
2. 1 in.
3. 5 in.
4. 3 in.

Reteach 75, page 133

1. a
2. b
3. b
4. a
5. a
6. b
7. b
8. a
9. a
10. a

Reteach 76, page 134

1. 24°F
2. 82°F
3. 60°F
4. 8°F
5. 35°F
6. 77°F

Reteach 77, page 135

1. 10 cm
2. 8 cm
3. m
4. cm
5. km
6. cm

Reteach 78, page 136

1. 90 g
2. 3 g
3. 10 kg
4. 1 g
5. 1 kg
6. 10 g
7. 1 L

(Reteach 78 continued)

8. 2 L
9. 100 mL
10. 100 L
11. 10 mL
12. 200 mL

Reteach 79, page 137

1. 37°C
2. 23°C
3. 40°C
4. 10°C
5. 31°C
6. 18°C

Reteach 80, page 138

1. 16 yd
2. 12 in.
3. 18 ft
4. 17 yd
5. 12 in.
6. 19 ft

Reteach 81, page 139

1. 4
2. 3
3. 5
4. 6
5. 9
6. 8
7. 5
8. 8
9. 10

Reteach 82, page 140

1. 3
2. 4
3. 4
4. 5
5. 3
6. 5
7. 4
8. 5
9. 6

Reteach 83, page 141

1. 328
2. 51
3. 417
4. 628
5. >
6. <
7. =
8. >
9. <
10. <

(Reteach 83 continued)

11. <
12. <
13. <

Reteach 84, page 142

1. 0.6
2. 0.2
3. 0.8
4. 0.3
5. 0.1
6. 0.5
7. 0.9
8. 0.3
9. 0.4
10. 0.1
11. 0.8
12. 0.2
13. 0.7
14. 0.9
15. 0.6

Reteach 85, page 143

1. 2.7
2. 1.5
3. 2.3
4. 6.5
5. 0.7
6. 4.8
7. 4.9
8. 1.3
9. 0.2
10. 7.1
11. 9.5
12. 6.4
13. 3.5
14. 8.2
15. 12.6
16. 6.1
17. 2.3
18. 5.9

Reteach 86, page 144

1. 0.67
2. 0.25
3. 0.58
4. 0.30
5. 0.04
6. 0.91
7. 0.64
8. 0.50
9. 0.33
10. 0.11
11. 0.85
12. 0.02
13. 0.75
14. 0.94
15. 0.43

Answer Key • Reteach Worksheets

Reteach 87, page 145

1. >
2. <
3. >
4. <
5. <
6. =
7. >
8. >
9. >
10. <

Reteach 88, page 146

1. 10.8
2. 2.8
3. 37.0
4. 54.3
5. 13.6
6. 42.8
7. 81.3
8. 14.5

Reteach 89, page 147

1. $5.68
2. $4.72
3. $14.16
4. $12.90
5. $11.84
6. $16.17
7. $15.25
8. $8.32
9. $.86
10. $.32
11. $.53
12. $.45
13. $.37
14. $.46
15. $.41
16. $.61

Reteach 90, page 148

1. 0.3 or 0.30; $.30
2. 0.8 or 0.80; $.80
3. 0.7 or 0.70; $.70
4. 0.25; $.25
5. 0.5 or 0.50; $.50

Answer Key • Extension Worksheets

Extension 1, page 151

1. 9,852
2. 7,643
3. 3,478
4. 65,310
5. 235,689
6. 754,320
7. 2,397
8. 43,251
9. 5,026
10. 48,753

Extension 2, page 152

1. 27
2. 420
3. 88
4. 503
5. S
6. h or i

Extension 3, page 153

1. 30 + 30 + 50
2. 30 + 30 + 30 + 30
3. 30 + 50 + 50
4. 30 + 30 + 30 + 50
5. 50 + 50 + 50 or 30 + 30 + 30 + 30 + 30
6. 30 + 30 + 50 + 50
7. 30 + 30 + 30 + 30 + 50
8. 30 + 50 + 50 + 50 or 30 + 30 + 30 + 30 + 30 + 30
9. 30 + 30 + 30 + 50 + 50
10. 50 + 50 + 50 + 50
11. 40 + 70
12. 40 + 40 + 40
13. not possible
14. 70 + 70
15. 40 + 40 + 70
16. 40 + 40 + 40 + 40
17. not possible
18. 40 + 70 + 70
19. 40 + 40 + 40 + 70
20. 40 + 40 + 40 + 40 + 40
21. 130; 170

Extension 4, page 154

1. 51
2. 63
3. 19
4. 37
5. 45
6. 79
7. 72
8. 35
9. 25
10. 32

(Extension 4 continued)

11. 51
12. 40
13. 42
14. 74
15. 42
16. 31
17. 54
18. 74

Extension 5, page 155

1. 26
2. 17
3. 27
4. 9
5. 43
6. 25
7. 35
8. 77
9. 58
10. 17
11. 23
12. 42
13. 18
14. 36
15. 65
16. 39
17. 28
18. 22

Extension 6, page 156

1. 2, 4, 6, 8, 10, 12, 14, 16, 18, 20, 22, 24, 26, 28, 30, 32, 34, 36, 38, 40, 42, 44, 46, 48, 50, 52, 54, 56, 58, 60, 62, 64, 66, 68, 70, 72, 74, 76, 78, 80, 82, 84, 86, 88, 90, 92, 94, 96, 98, 100
2. 3, 6, 9, 12, 15, 18, 21, 24, 27, 30, 33, 36, 39, 42, 45, 48, 51, 54, 57, 60, 63, 66, 69, 72, 75, 78, 81, 84, 87, 90, 93, 96, 99
3. 4, 8, 12, 16, 20, 24, 28, 32, 36, 40, 44, 48, 52, 56, 60, 64, 68, 72, 76, 80, 84, 88, 92, 96, 100
4. 5, 10, 15, 20, 25, 30, 35, 40, 45, 50, 55, 60, 65, 70, 75, 80, 85, 90, 95, 100
5. 5, 10, 15, 20, 25, 30, 35, 40, 45, 50, 55, 60, 65, 70, 75, 80, 85, 90, 95, 100; All the numbers end in 0 or in 5.
6. 60
7. 7
8. Answers will vary.

Extension 7, page 157

1. 12; 21; Multiply by 3.
2. 10; 11; Add 5.
3. 3; 6; Subtract 9.
4. 12; 18; Multiply by 2.
5. Answers will vary.

Extension 8, page 158

1. Possible figure:

2. Possible figure:

Extension 9, page 159

1. slide
2. Check students' drawings.
3. flip
4. flip or turn

Extension 10, page 160

1. No; It usually rains only one day in April.
2. No; The graph does not show the temperatures.
3. Possible answer: The weather will probably be hot and sunny. The weather is already very nice in April, so the resort may be near the equator.
4. Skiing is guaranteed for every day but Sunday.
5. It will probably remain between 15° and 25°, because that is the most frequent temperature range.

Extension 11, page 161

1. 4 in.; 8 in.
2. 6 in.
3. 3 in.; 9 in.
4. 2 in.; 10 in.
5. 2
6. 4
7. 3
8. 2

Extension 12, page 162

1. 5 + 5; 5
   5 + 4; 4
   4 + 1; 1
   2 + 4 + 4; 2
   5 + 4 + 1; 10
2. 4 × 4; 4
   3 × 4; 3
   3 × 5; 5
   5 × 1; 5
3. Answers will vary. Possible answer: 3 + 8 = 11; 8 − 3 = 5
4. Answers will vary. Possible answer: 4 × 5 = 20; 20 ÷ 5 = 4

Extension 13, page 163

1. 2 × 7
2. 3 × 7
3. 2 × 2 × 7
4. 2 × 3 × 7
5. 2 × 2 × 2 × 7
6. 3 × 3 × 7
7. 3 × 5
8. 5 × 7
9. 3 × 3 × 5
10. 7 × 7
11. 2 × 2
12. 2 × 3
13. 2 × 2 × 2
14. 2 × 5
15. 2 × 2 × 3
16. 3 × 5
17. 2 × 2 × 2 × 2
18. 2 × 3 × 3
19. 2 × 2 × 5
20. 2 × 2 × 2 × 3
21. 5 × 5
22. 3 × 3 × 3
23. 2 × 3 × 5
24. 2 × 2 × 3 × 3

Extension 14, page 164

1. 90
2. 80
3. 80
4. 50
5. 600
6. 800
7. 900
8. 600
9. $.80
10. $1.00

Answer Key • Extension Worksheets

(Extension 14 continued)
11. $1.50
12. $.90
13. about 40 minutes
14. about $2.40

Extension 15, page 165

1. 7; No.
  8 R2; No.
  9 R1; Yes.
  5 R3; No.
  6 R4; No.
  7 R2; Yes.
2. 37
3. 44; 36, 44; 44; 44
4. 27, 36; 44, 36; 36; 36
5. No, the remainder can never be greater than the divisor.

Extension 16, page 166

1. 6; 60; 8; 80; 30
2. 55
3. b
4. b
5. a
6. a
7. 30
8. 15
9. 10
10. 20
11. 10
12. 20
13. 30
14. 20
15. 20
16. 30
17. 30
18. 20
19. 40
20. 30
21. 70
22. 30

Extension 17, page 167

1.–6. Answers will vary.
  7. Possible answer: I looked for an object about the size of my hand.
  8. Answers will vary.

Extension 18, page 168

1. 21
2. 16
3. 19
4. Estimates will vary.

Extension 19, page 169

1. 7
2. 18
3. 44
4. 27
5. 4
6. 11
7. 93
8. 2
9. 36
10. 78
11. 63
12. 59
13. 2.3
14. 4.3
15. 10.5
16. 5.5
17. 0.8
18. 7.7
19. 9.8
20. 24.5
21. 0.7
22. 15.7
23. 39.3
24. 43.1

Extension 20, page 170

1. 0.1; $\frac{2}{10}$; 0.3; $\frac{3}{10}$; 0.4; 0.5; $\frac{5}{10}$; 0.7; $\frac{7}{10}$; 0.8; $\frac{9}{10}$
2. 0.1; 0.5; 0.7; 0.9
3. 0.2; 0.4; 0.6; 0.8
4. $\frac{1}{4}$, $\frac{1}{2}$, $\frac{3}{4}$
5. >
6. <
7. <
8. >
9. =
10. >
11. >
12. <
13. <